THE ASSESSMENT OF FUNCTIONAL LIVING SKILLS

(The AFLS®)

An assessment, skills tracking system, and curriculum guide
for skills that are essential for independence

Vocational Skills
Assessment Protocol

by

James W. Partington, Ph.D., BCBA-D

and

Michael M. Mueller, Ph.D., BCBA-D

May 2015

Version 1.0

Vocational Skills Assessment Protocol

An assessment, skills tracking system, and curriculum guide
for skills that are essential for independence

May 2015
Version 1.0

Partington, James W., and Mueller, Michael M.

This book is intended to be sold only to individuals as a part of a two-book set that includes the Assessment of Functional Living Skills Guide (The AFLS® Guide) or to individuals who have previously purchased The AFLS® Guide. If you have obtained a copy of this AFLS® Vocational Skills Assessment Protocol without The AFLS® Guide, you are advised to obtain a copy of it so that you will have a better understanding of the content of this AFLS® Protocol and its intended purpose. The AFLS® Guide provides critical information regarding how to conduct the assessment. It also contains important information regarding precautions that must be observed during the assessment process, when determining a learner's current skill level, and when attempting to teach new functional skills.

The AFLS® is an assessment tool based on a criterion-referenced set of skills that can demonstrate a learner's current functional skill repertoire and provide tracking information for the progressive development of these skills throughout the lifespan. Although the skills listed in this tool are important vocational skills that will lead to greater levels of overall independence and employment opportunities, some individuals with developmental delays will not be able to learn and competently master all of these skills. Additionally, the attainment of all the skills by a person with a developmental disability does not mean that the individual will necessarily be able to live independently or obtain employment. Decisions regarding the learner's readiness for various vocational or employment opportunities should be made by the learner, by family members or other caregivers, and professionals who are familiar with the learner's ability to safely perform work-related activities. This protocol is not a diagnostic tool and should not be used for determining diagnostic labels, eligibility for services, and should not be used as the sole source of information for educational decision making or vocational placement. It is not within the scope of this instrument to determine the appropriateness of any educational goals and objectives, nor the priority of a learner's needs. Rather, it is recommended that users confer with a trained and experienced professional to evaluate which skills can safely be directly assessed, to determine appropriate educational priorities, and to assist with teaching and other programming decisions.

ISBN: **978-0-9882493-6-3**

Publishers:

Behavior Analysts, Inc.
309 Lennon Lane, Suite 104
Walnut Creek, CA 94598
partingtonbehavioranalysts.com
(925) 210-9378
FAX (925) 210-0436

Stimulus Publications
2470 Windy Hill Rd., Suite 300
Marietta, GA 30067
www.stimuluspublications.com
(877) 221-6099
FAX (770) 956-2919

PLEASE READ THIS WARNING

**It is very important that the user of this assessment protocol reads *The AFLS®
Guide* prior to attempts to assess or teach any of the skills listed in this protocol.**
Everyone faces some inherent risks while performing most daily activities. We come into
contact with situations that require quick judgment, "reading" split-second sources of
information while making decisions in complex situations, and weighing risks in order to
avoid danger. From the time we wake in the morning until the time we go to bed at night,
constant risk and danger is present, but avoided, for most of us because of our
experiences, training, and cognitive abilities. Individuals with autism and developmental
delays face *increased* risks of injury because they might not be aware of, understand, or
maintain focused attention during potentially dangerous situations or while performing
certain activities. As such, caregivers must always be responsible for ensuring the safety
of individuals with developmental delays. Some of the activities that are included in the
assessment protocols may not be safe to directly assess for some individuals.
Furthermore, attempts to assess or teach some of the skills may also have potential safety
risks for the caregiver. Therefore, any attempt to determine a learner's level of skills, or
to teach such skills, must ensure the safety of both the learner and the caregiver. Your
knowledge of the learner, the learner's history, your own level of comfort in various
situations, and common sense should help determine your approach. Never place a
learner at risk, even momentarily, to obtain assessment data.

**BECAUSE SOME LEARNERS MAY NOT HAVE THE COGNITIVE SKILLS
AND SUBSEQUENT JUDGEMENT ESSENTIAL FOR THEM TO BE ABLE TO
SAFELY ENGAGE IN CERTAIN ACTIVITIES, SOME OF THE ITEMS IN THIS
PROTOCOL MAY NOT BE APPROPRIATE TO DIRECTLY ASSESS OR
TEACH TO SOME INDIVIDUALS. IT IS THE RESPONSIBILITY OF
PARENTS, CAREGIVERS, AND TEACHERS TO ALWAYS ENSURE THAT AN
INDIVIDUAL IS PROTECTED FROM HARM.**

- **DO NOT PLACE LEARNERS AT RISK**
- **DO NOT LEAVE LEARNERS UNATTENDED**
- **DO NOT EXPOSE LEARNERS TO DANGEROUS SITUATIONS**
- **CLOSELY SUPERVISE LEARNERS THROUGHOUT ENTIRE ASSESSMENT**

Overview of The AFLS®

The Assessment of Functional Living Skills (The AFLS®) is an assessment, skills tracking system, and curriculum guide for the development of essential skills for achieving independence. Thus, *The AFLS®* contains task analyses of many of the skills essential for participation in a wide range of family, school, community, and work environments. The *AFLS®* is comprised of multiple documents including *The AFLS® Guide* and six unique assessment protocols: Basic Living Skills, Home Skills, Community Participation Skills, School Skills, Vocational Skills, and Independent Living Skills. Each assessment protocol contains a variety of skill areas to thoroughly assess the functional skills across a wide range of settings and throughout a learner's lifespan. Finally, a forthcoming set of companion teaching manuals will contain task analyses, teaching strategies, and prompting techniques for each assessment protocol that will be beneficial to optimize instruction of the skills in each area.

Functional skills are commonly thought of as skills that if not mastered *by* the learner, will have to be done *for* the learner. These are essential, practical, everyday skills of daily living. Although some functional skills are routine and even mundane at times, without the demonstration of these skills, a person is dependent on others for care. On the other hand, the more a learner can master, a greater level of independence is possible and additional opportunities open up in academic achievement, school options, academic placement choices, peer relations, social interactions, self reliance, self esteem, sports, leisure, community participation, living and housing arrangements, job choices, etc. Every protocol of *The AFLS®* is designed to ensure that caregivers and professionals provide learners with the very best opportunities to learn how to do tasks for themselves in a broad array of real-world settings.

The AFLS® Guide provides information regarding the background, development, target populations, ages, and requirements for conducting the assessment. Descriptions and examples of the language used in the assessment, terminology, and intent of different sections are described in *The Guide* and should be read prior to completing this assessment protocol. Most importantly, *The AFLS® Guide* provides detailed information required for conducting the assessment, accurately scoring the assessment, and completing the skills tracking grid for easy analysis and comparison of learner outcomes. *The AFLS® Guide* also provides critical information regarding learner and caregiver safety. Additionally, *The AFLS® Guide* provides strategies to assist parents, caregivers, educators, and other professionals to use the information obtained from the completed assessment protocol to develop an effective individualized functional skills development program.

About The AFLS® Vocational Skills

Assessment Protocol

The current assessment protocol, *The AFLS Vocational Skills Assessment Protocol,* provides caregivers and professionals with criterion-referenced information regarding a learner's ability to prepare for the workplace and participate independently in a variety of vocational roles and settings. *The AFLS Vocational Skills Assessment Protocol* reviews skills that will allow a learner to pursue, obtain, and participate in meaningful and gainful employment in a variety of settings. Although some individuals with developmental delays will only be able to participate in supported work settings, there are many other individuals who can learn the skills necessary to earn significant incomes in highly specialized fields such as graphics design, computer programming, and the performing arts. Therefore, the skills included in this assessment protocol can be used to help facilitate an individual's opportunities in a wide range of areas so as to reach their potential in the workforce.

The protocol focuses both on the "soft" skills required for participation in many jobs and includes language and communication skills, social skills and interactions, and work place etiquette. "Hard" skills from many different job areas are included so that the skills required to fill many different roles and responsibilities in a wide range of workplace settings can be evaluated. Further, the lists of both soft and hard skills can serve as a training curriculum that if followed, could lead to successful demonstration of skills required for many vocational settings.

Beginning with the skills necessary to find and choose jobs, and attaining a wide variety of job-specific skills, this assessment protocol evaluates a learner's readiness for employment and of the skills required to find jobs and participate in the workforce. There are eighteen skill areas covered in this protocol. They include Job Search, Interview, Basic Skills, Coworker Relations, Workplace Safety, Fixed Activity Skills, Custodial and Cleaning, Laundry, Retail, Support Personnel, Office Skills, Computer Skills, Restaurant Skills, Restaurant Kitchen, Warehouse, Tools, Trades and Construction, and Landscaping.

Several sections of this assessment protocol evaluate skills that are universally important for all vocational training opportunities and actual employment. Individuals with developmental delays and autism can hold a wide variety of positions that encompass all possible fields. It was not possible to cover all aspects of every job responsibility a learner might have during employment. However, those chosen for assessment in this protocol were included based on our research of where individuals with disabilities tend to find employment. Feedback and recommendations were also obtained from a variety of administrators and professionals who have dedicated their careers to supporting vocational settings with learners with special needs. Reviewers who work in vocational placement agencies provided additional suggestions about skills and job positions.

Many jobs require safety certifications, licensure, state or local governmental oversight, additional inspection, and/or regulatory provisions. It is not the intent of this assessment to circumvent those required aspects of holding any position or performing any tasks. Compliance with field or governmental mandates should occur, if required, *prior* to any skill assessment or skill demonstration that may contradict those requirements. *The AFLS Vocational Skills Assessment Protocol* is not a job certifying task list nor is it a job completion certification program. The skills listed in this assessment are merely to assess whether the skills currently are part of a learner's repertoire regardless of whether or not a learner may or may not need those skills as part of any, separate credentialing process.

Many of the skills listed in this assessment carry very serious inherent risks, including death, if directly assessed, assessed improperly, or without adequate supervision. Safety during any assessment of these skills is of critical importance. All users of this assessment protocol are directed back to the AFLS® Guide for additional safety warnings and advisories. Do not directly assess or test the skills in this protocol if there is a chance of injury. NEVER put a learner at risk, even momentarily, to obtain assessment data. If it is unknown whether a leaner has a particular skill and directly testing the skill might be unsafe, DO NOT test the skill. Err on the side of caution at all times.

Special Scoring Considerations

The criteria listed in this skills assessment protocol often list "with only verbal prompts" as a component of the lowest criterion. "Verbal prompts" can take many different forms, and, many professionals who provide services to learners do not use a "vocal" prompt, but might instead point to a visual schedule reminder, visual prompt, or something similar. For the purpose of this assessment, if a service provider uses a visual prompt as a first prompt in a sequence, score the use of that prompt as a "verbal" prompt. To help clarify how the item was scored, it might be helpful to include this information (e.g., "We scored pointing to a visual schedule as a verbal prompt for this item") in the comment column so future assessors or anyone looking at the protocol can understand how the scoring of any particular item might have varied from the wording of the item being assessed.

The most important outcomes for your learner are those that are individualized by caregivers, job supervisors, and other professionals who know, understand, and respect the learner, and maintain the learner's best interests in the forefront of the assessment process. Answering each item carefully will demonstrate what the learner is able do, and actually does, and will result in the most accurate picture of the learner's ability and needs.

The Vocational Skills Repertoires

Specific repertoires that are included in *The AFLS Vocational Skills Assessment Protocol* are:

Job Search
    The learner must be able to determine interests and practical variables related to employment to ensure that a job will be a good fit with the learner's overall living situation. Search engines, job listing services, newspapers, and "help wanted" signs on store front windows can all be relevant job search locations. Determining what a job is, whether it compliments a learner's interests and current skill set, proximity to the learner's residence, etc. are important in considering a position.

Interview
    For many positions, performance in a face-to-face interview might be the most important variable in obtaining a job. The learner needs to have knowledge of the company, articulation of relevant past vocational and personal experiences, demonstration of active listening skills, attention to the interviewer, ability to answer questions, ask questions and take notes, etc. Arranging an interview and practicing skills in a mock interview format are covered in this section.

Basic Skills
    Regardless of the position a learner might ultimately take in the job market, certain skills are relevant and universally required for maintaining meaningful employment and a positive work experience. Hygiene, dress, manners, compliance, dependability, trustworthiness, learning new skills quickly, and other required workplace skills are assessed in this section.

Coworker Relations
    The ability to interact with others in a socially acceptable manner is essential for successful participation in employment activities. Workplace interaction is required in most positions and the learner's ability to participate effectively in those interactions is of critical importance. Recognizing workplace hierarchy, identifying supervisors, describing roles and responsibilities of coworkers, dealing with workplace conflict, complying with work demands, responding appropriately to feedback, giving feedback in a tactful manner, and other interactional skills are evaluated in this section.

Workplace Safety
    Workplace safety is of critical importance to any individual participating in vocational activities. As in everyday life, there are almost constant risks and dangers that exist in certain employment roles and responsibilities. This section assesses the learner's ability to recognize, avoid, or respond to a wide range of scenarios and situations in which safety is a primary issue. Safety issues related to heat, cold, heights, moving vehicles, flammable liquids, toxic substances, fumes, sharp items, moving machinery, and more are assessed.

Fixed Activity Skills

Commonly and formerly referred to as "prevocational" or "workshop" tasks, the Fixed Activity Skills section includes the assessment of skills such as folding, collating or inserting paper products. Also covered are assembly tasks such as placing items into small bags or boxes for distribution and binding tasks such as using twist ties.

Custodial and Cleaning

Many common and advanced cleaning tasks are assessed in this section. It includes different areas to be cleaned and maintained such as offices, bathrooms, and hotel rooms. Maintenance, repairs, and daily upkeep of these various settings are included. More advanced skills such as privacy issues, confidentiality, and private or locked storage areas are assessed along with issues of security and building access.

Laundry

Positions that involve washing clothes and bedding are common. This section assesses the pre-washing skills of sorting and determining what and how to wash, the use of washing machines and dryers, along with removing and folding clothes or bedding.

Retail

The retail industry is a major vocational area for learners with disabilities and the range of positions and skills required is even more varied. Settings include grocery stores, clothing stores, and other shops and locations. Behind the scenes skills such as stocking items, unpacking items, inventory control, receiving inventory, hanging up clothes, and more are assessed. Cash register skills, customer interactions, problem solving, and responding to customer inquiries are included.

Support Personnel

Learner participation in employment activities centered on caring for the very young or the very old are assessed. Helping classroom or recreational staff move and operate equipment, serve snacks and drinks, and participate and monitor children or residents are assessed.

Office Skills

Skills assessed in this section include the use of basic office machines and tools such as staplers, pens, paper clips, etc. Printing, copying, scanning, faxing, and troubleshooting those processes when problems arise are also assessed. Filing and sorting and more complex discriminations related to everyday office environments are included. Finally, important language and social interactions required for successful participation in office jobs are assessed.

Computer Skills

Computer technology is utilized in many fields of employment and in many specific job positions. For many skills, basic computer use and understanding is a requirement. This section assesses basic computer skills and operation along with common software familiarity and use of spreadsheets and word processing applications. Safety and security issues are also assessed.

Restaurant Skills

The roles in food service and restaurants are widely varied and the skills required to participate in those roles involve considerable amounts of interaction and coordination with others. Skills related to bussing tables, washing dishes, waiting tables, hosting tables, and daily upkeep routines are areas that are assessed in this section.

Restaurant Kitchen

Roles in restaurants include planning, preparing, cooking and storing food as well as kitchen safety. This section assesses the aspects of restaurant employment that centers around actual food preparation and creation.

Warehouse

Issues and skills related to boxes in a warehouse are assessed in this section. This includes picking up packages, packing boxes, shipping packages, finding the location in a warehouse or storage facility, inventory management, and using fork lifts and transportation for inventory.

Tools

Tool usage is required in many of the building, construction, landscaping, and related fields. To be a valued employee in these types of positions, basic and more advanced tool usage might be required. This section assesses the learner's ability to use a wide variety of common hand and power tools.

Trades and Construction

The building and construction trades are varied and individualized skill areas. In this section, several prominent skills related to each area are included so that basic and more advanced skill repertoires typical of these different areas can be assessed and a curriculum for training can be outlined. General hand tool use, power tool use, lifting, carrying, and other common skills are assessed first. The other sections within the broader categories include drywall, painting, roofing, electricity, plumbing, carpeting, and automotive skills.

Landscaping

Caring for plants, gardening, removing garden waste, using hand tools, using power tools, and other common landscaping and lawn maintenance skills are assessed. Fertilizer use, pesticide use and safety, mowing and caring for lawns are included.

Table of Contents

Assessment of Functional Living Skills
Skills Tracking System

Vocational Skills

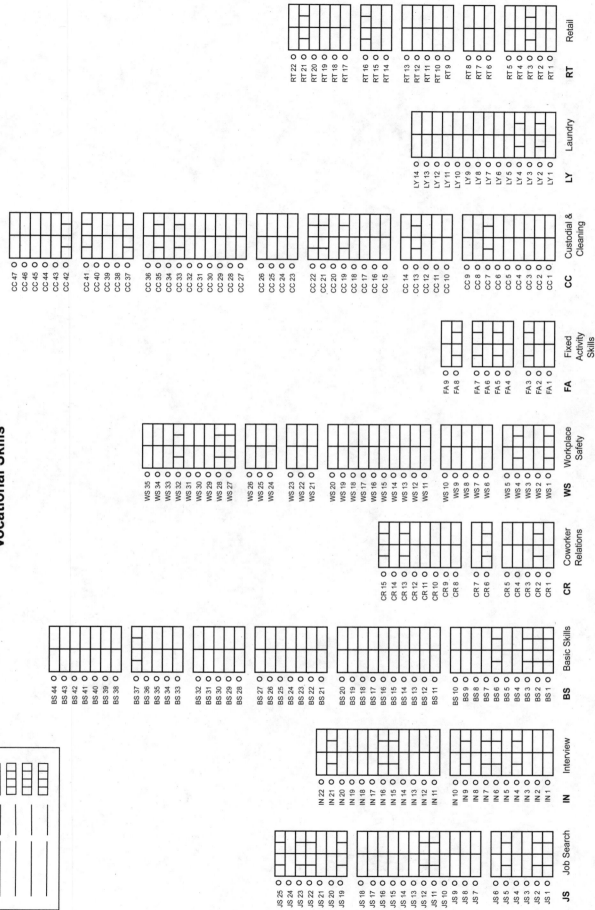

Learner:

Assessor

Date

Color Code

JS Job Search

IN Interview

BS Basic Skills

CR Coworker Relations

WS Workplace Safety

FA Fixed Activity Skills

CC Custodial & Cleaning

LY Laundry

RT Retail

Assessment of Functional Living Skills
Skills Tracking System
Vocational Skills

Learner: _____

Assessor _____

Date _____

Color Code

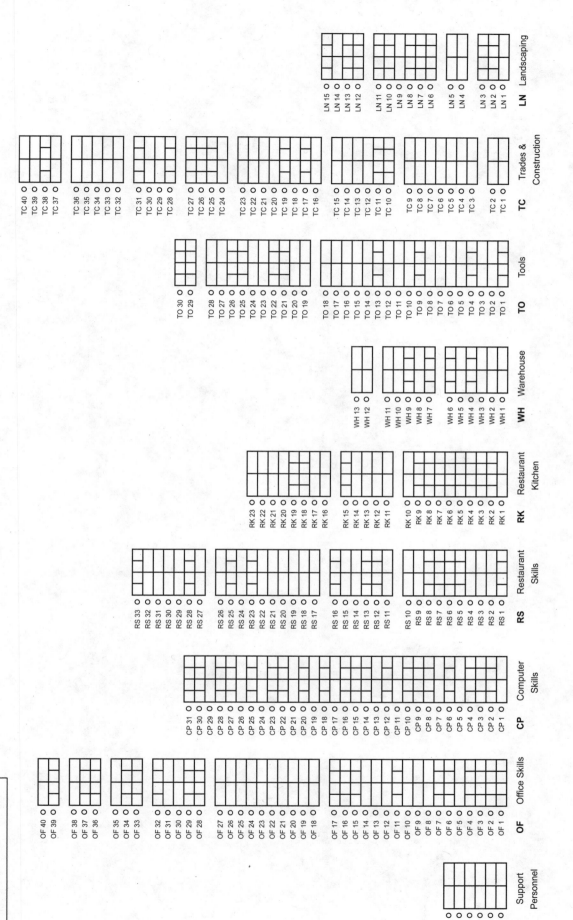

SP Support Personnel

OF Office Skills

CP Computer Skills

RS Restaurant Skills

RK Restaurant Kitchen

WH Warehouse

TO Tools

TC Trades & Construction

LN Landscaping

The Assessment of Functional Living Skills - The AFLS®

Job Search

Awareness of personal attributes

TASK	SCORE	TASK NAME	TASK OBJECTIVE	QUESTION	EXAMPLE	CRITERIA	COMMENT
JS 1	0 1 2 3 4 0 1 2 3 4 0 1 2 3 4 0 1 2 3 4	Identifies own strengths and weaknesses	Learner will identify own strengths and weaknesses.	Can learner identify own strengths and weaknesses?	I'm great with computers and numbers, but I'm not very good at talking to people on the phone or working outside when it's hot	4= states at least 3 personal strengths and 2 personal weakness and 3 work-related strengths and weaknesses, 3= states 1 personal strength and 1 personal weakness and 2 work-related strengths and weaknesses, 2= states 2 work-related strengths and weaknesses, 1= states 1 work-related strength and weakness	
JS 2	0 1 2 3 4 0 1 2 3 4 0 1 2 3 4 0 1 2 3 4	Identifies job-related interests	Learner will Identify job-related interests.	Can learner Identify job-related interests?	I'm interested in working with animals, working in a garden, working outside, but I'm not interested in computers, working in an office, working with paper and printers, etc.	4= states 5 job-related interests, 3= states 4 job-related interests, 2= states 3 job-related interests, 1= states 2 job-related interests	
JS 3	0 1 2 0 1 2 0 1 2 0 1 2	Identifies jobs that correspond to job-related interests	Learner will identify jobs that correspond to job-related interests.	Can learner identify jobs that correspond to job-related interests?	Vet assistant, data entry clerk, graphic artist, web designer, park maintenance staff, waitress, etc.	2= states at least 4 types of jobs that correspond to learner's job-related interests, 1= states at least 2 types of jobs that correspond to learner's job-related interests	
JS 4	0 1 2 0 1 2 0 1 2 0 1 2	Identifies qualities or attributes that would rule out certain jobs or positions	Learner will identify jobs that are not good fits with learner's preferences.	Can learner identify jobs that are not good fits based on learner's preferences?	Does not like spiders so should not pursue landscaping work, wakes up late so should not pursue 1st shift	2= states at least 4 types of jobs that do not fit well with learner's preferences, 1= states at least 2 types of jobs that do not fit well with learner's preferences	
JS 5	0 1 2 3 4 0 1 2 3 4 0 1 2 3 4 0 1 2 3 4	Gives a clear description of specific types of jobs	Learner will describe job expectations and responsibilities for different positions.	Can learner describe job expectations and responsibilities for different positions?	Basic roles and responsibilities, expectations, features, setting, etc. A waitress works in a restaurant by taking orders from customers, bringing their food and drinks, and attending to their needs during the meal	4= describes at least 8 different job positions, 3= describes at least 6 different job positions, 2= describes at least 4 different job positions, 1= describes 2 job positions	
JS 6	0 1 2 0 1 2 0 1 2 0 1 2	Recognizes help wanted signs in community	Learner will recognize help wanted signs in community.	Does learner recognize help wanted signs in community?		2= identifies position offered in help wanted signs seen in the community and determines whether position is a relevant possibility, 1= identifies help wanted signs in storefronts, windows, or signage that indicate company is hiring	

The AFLS® - Vocational Skills Protocol

The Assessment of Functional Living Skills - The AFLS®

Job Search (Continued)

Looking for jobs

TASK	SCORE	TASK NAME	TASK OBJECTIVE	QUESTION	EXAMPLE	CRITERIA	COMMENT
JS 7	0 1 2 0 1 2 0 1 2 0 1 2	Stops in and inquires about employment	Learner will stop in to inquire about employment.	Can learner stop in to inquire about potential employment?	Sees help wanted sign in window of store, walks in to inquire about potential job opportunities	2= independently enters potential job site, asks to speak to manager, and inquires about potential employment, 1= enters potential job site, asks to speak to manager, and inquires about potential employment with the assistance of a caregiver	
JS 8	0 1 2 0 1 2 0 1 2 0 1 2	Networks for job search	Learner will network for job search.	Does learner network for job search?		2= identifies at least 3 people who might be likely to lead to work opportunities and communicates with them about employment, 1= states name of at least 1 person who might be a contact for future employment	
JS 9	0 1 2 0 1 2 0 1 2 0 1 2	Calls to inquire about employment	Learner will call contact to inquire about employment.	Can learner call contact to inquire about employment?		2= independently calls job contact to inquire about position, 1= calls job contact to inquire about position when provided with verbal prompts or coached on what to say	
JS 10	0 1 2 0 1 2 0 1 2 0 1 2	Emails to inquire about a position	Learner will email to inquire about a job opening.	Can learner email to inquire about a job opening?		2= emails job contact to inquire about position using acceptable written text and format, 1= emails job contact to inquire about position using acceptable written text and format or appropriately with verbal assistance from caregiver	
JS 11	0 1 2 3 4 0 1 2 3 4 0 1 2 3 4 0 1 2 3 4	Searches for job openings	Learner will search for job openings in paper want ads and computer job postings.	Can learner search for job openings in paper want ads and computer job postings?	Monster.com, Craigslist.com, Careerbuilder.com, searches individual companies' websites for employment possibilities, etc.	4= searches for employment from 3 or more computer or paper want ads/job search locations and identifies employment opportunities appropriate for learner's skills, 3= searches for employment from 1 computer and 1 paper want ads/job search location and identifies employment opportunities appropriate for learner's skills, 2= searches for employment from 1 computer or paper want ads/job search location, 1= states name of computer job search location or finds want ads section in paper	

The AFLS® - Vocational Skills Protocol

The Assessment of Functional Living Skills - The AFLS®

Job Search (Continued)

TASK	SCORE	TASK NAME	TASK OBJECTIVE	QUESTION	EXAMPLE	CRITERIA	COMMENT
JS 12	0 1 2 3 4 0 1 2 3 4 0 1 2 3 4 0 1 2 3 4	Abbreviations in want ads and job postings	Learner will state meaning of abbreviations in want ads and job postings.	Can learner state meaning of abbreviations in ads?	Ben., Yrs., Wk., w/, FT, PT, Attn., WPM, info., M-F, Immed., Mgr., Lic., Pd, 1st shift, 2nd shift, 3rd shift, Hrly, Col. Grad, by appt, EOE, etc.	4= states meaning of 20 different want ad abbreviations, 3= states meaning of 15 different want ad abbreviations, 2= states meaning of 10 different want ad abbreviations, 1= states meaning of 5 different want ad abbreviations	
JS 13	0 1 2 0 1 2 0 1 2 0 1 2	Determines if learner has skills required for the job	Learner will determine if learner has skills required for the job.	Can learner determine if learner has skills required for the job?	Job requires ability to drive and I have my driver's license and a car. Job requires use of a jack hammer and I used to use a jack hammer in my old job	2= states skill requirements for posted job and makes accurate determination about whether learner possesses those requirements, 1= states skill requirements for posted job and determines whether learner possesses those requirements with assistance from caregiver	
JS 14	0 1 2 0 1 2 0 1 2 0 1 2	Determines if learner has requirements for the job	Learner will determine if possesses job requirements.	Can learner determine if possesses job requirements?	Certifications, degrees, years of experience, etc.	2= states requirements for posted job and makes accurate determination about whether learner meets those requirements, 1= states requirements for posted job and determines whether learner meets those requirements with assistance from caregiver	
JS 15	0 1 2 0 1 2 0 1 2 0 1 2	Considers job in relation to current interests	Learner will decide if job activities fit with personal interests.	Can learner decide if job activities fit with personal interests?		2= makes decision about whether activities of job fit with learner's job interests, 1= makes decision about whether activities of job fit with learner's job interests with assistance of caregiver	
JS 16	0 1 2 0 1 2 0 1 2 0 1 2	Analyzes whether job is close enough to residence to be practical	Learner will analyze whether job is close enough to residence to be practical.	Can learner analyze whether job is close enough to residence to be practical?	Inputs job site address into computer map program, computes distance from residence, decides that a bus stop is 2 blocks away from job location, etc.	2= determines whether job site is within reasonable distance and manageable given current transportation issues, 1= determines address of job site	

The AFLS® - Vocational Skills Protocol

The Assessment of Functional Living Skills - The AFLS®

Job Search (Continued)

TASK	SCORE	TASK NAME	TASK OBJECTIVE	QUESTION	EXAMPLE	CRITERIA	COMMENT
JS 17	0 1 2 0 1 2 0 1 2 0 1 2	Researches a job position	Learner will research a job position.	Can learner research a job position?		2= states information about a job to include the salary, wage, benefits, hours per week (full or part time), shift (start and end time), and other relevant variables of the position, 1= states pay and hours of work	
JS 18	0 1 2 0 1 2 0 1 2 0 1 2	Researches a company	Learner will research a company.	Can learner research a company?		2= states information about primary products or services company provides, size, structure, public/private, and location of headquarters for a company, 1= states information about primary products or services company provides	

Applying for jobs

TASK	SCORE	TASK NAME	TASK OBJECTIVE	QUESTION	EXAMPLE	CRITERIA	COMMENT
JS 19	0 1 2 3 4 0 1 2 3 4 0 1 2 3 4 0 1 2 3 4	Prepares a resume	Learner will prepare a professional resume to submit for employment.	Can learner prepare a professional resume to submit for employment?		4= prepares and updates resume independently, 3= provides all relevant information but requires verbal prompts to assist entering information into computer, 2= provides personal information and job history for someone else to enter information into computer, 1= provides personal information	
JS 20	0 1 2 0 1 2 0 1 2 0 1 2	Obtains letters of reference	Learner will obtain letters of reference.	Can learner obtain letters of reference?		2= calls, emails, or asks in person for letter of reference and provides enough information about intended position to secure the letter, 1= identifies people who are appropriate for use as a reference	
JS 21	0 1 2 0 1 2 0 1 2 0 1 2	Saves copies of previous work for future employees	Learner will save copies of previous work for future employees.	Can learner save copies of previous work for future employees?	Makes portfolio of graphic design projects, etc.	2= saves work samples to provide to others on request, 1= states type of samples that might be relevant for job application	
JS 22	0 1 2 3 4 0 1 2 3 4 0 1 2 3 4 0 1 2 3 4	Fills out an application for employment	Learner will fill out a job application.	Can learner fill out an application?	Writes within space allotted, input information into online employment application, etc.	4= neatly completes full application without assistance, 3= completes full application with verbal prompts, 2= completes personal information section without assistance but requires verbal prompts to provide other information, 1= requires verbal prompts to provide personal information	

The AFLS® - Vocational Skills Protocol

The Assessment of Functional Living Skills - The AFLS®

Job Search (Continued)

TASK	SCORE	TASK NAME	TASK OBJECTIVE	QUESTION	EXAMPLE	CRITERIA	COMMENT
JS 23	0 1 2 3 4 0 1 2 3 4 0 1 2 3 4 0 1 2 3 4	Prepares a cover letter	Learner will prepare a professional cover letter to submit for employment.	Can learner prepare a professional cover letter to submit for employment?	Uses a cover letter template and replaces the header, salutation, learner's address, contact person for position, sections with learner's information, etc.	4= prepares cover letter independently, 3= provides all relevant information but requires verbal prompts to assist entering information into computer, 2= provides most information into computer but requires someone else to enter information into computer, 1= articulates the reasons why the job is sought	
JS 24	0 1 2 0 1 2 0 1 2 0 1 2	Assembles a credential package	Learner will assemble a credential package.	Can learner assemble a credential package?	Letters or reference, reference list, resume, curriculum vita, cover letter, work samples, etc.	2= independently gathers cover letter, resume or vita, and previous work samples (if relevant), 1= states what is included in a credential package	
JS 25	0 1 2 3 4 0 1 2 3 4 0 1 2 3 4 0 1 2 3 4	Identifies community resources that may support job	Learner will identify community resources that may support job.	Can learner identify community resources that may support job?	Job coach, transportation, financial aid, training programs, government assistance programs	4= states need for support and searches online to identify resources in at least 2 different areas of support, 3= states need for support and uses online resources to identify 1 resource, 2= states need for support but requires verbal prompts to search for assistance, 1= requires verbal prompts to state need for support	

The AFLS® - Vocational Skills Protocol

The Assessment of Functional Living Skills - The AFLS®

Interview

Preparing for interview

TASK	SCORE	TASK NAME	TASK OBJECTIVE	QUESTION	EXAMPLE	CRITERIA	COMMENT
IN 1	0 1 2 0 1 2 0 1 2 0 1 2	Schedules interview	Learner will schedule the interview location and time.	Can learner schedule the interview location and time?	Learner chose time for interview, but needed a caregiver to make the phone call to set up the interview	2= schedules interview location, date, and time over the phone or via email, 1= requires only verbal prompts to schedule an interview	
IN 2	0 1 2 0 1 2 0 1 2 0 1 2	Uses calendar to record upcoming interviews	Learner will record job interviews on calendar.	Can learner use calendar to record job interviews?		2= records upcoming interviews on paper or computerized calendar, 1= records upcoming interviews on paper or computerized calendar with only verbal prompts	
IN 3	0 1 2 0 1 2 0 1 2 0 1 2	Arranges transportation to interview	Learner will arrange transportation to interview.	Can learner arrange transportation to interview?	Calls taxi and arranges to be picked up, calls reliable friend or family member, checks bus schedule for bus stop 1 block down the street, drives to interview, etc.	2= arranges transportation to interview, 1= arranges transportation to interview following verbal or written prompts by caregiver	
IN 4	0 1 2 3 4 0 1 2 3 4 0 1 2 3 4 0 1 2 3 4	Prepares a list of questions employer is likely to ask	Learner will prepare a list of questions an employer is likely to ask.	Can learner prepare a list of questions an employer is likely to ask?		4= prepares written list of at least 5 questions that might be asked during interview and rehearses answers out loud, 3= states at least 2 questions that might be asked during interview and rehearses answers out loud, 2= when given list of questions by caregiver, rehearses answers out loud, 1= when given list of questions by caregiver, rehearses answering those questions out loud with only verbal prompts	
IN 5	0 1 2 0 1 2 0 1 2 0 1 2	Requests caregiver present for interview	Learner will request the presence of a trusted person, advocate, or caregiver for interview.	Can learner request the presence of a caregiver for the interview?	Is feeling nervous about upcoming interview and contacts the company to seek approval for a third party to be present	2= contacts company to seek permission to bring a caregiver to interview and if approved, contacts caregiver to make arrangements for attendance, 1= tells caregiver about feelings of nervousness related to upcoming interview	

The AFLS® - Vocational Skills Protocol

The Assessment of Functional Living Skills - The AFLS®

Interview (Continued)

TASK	SCORE	TASK NAME	TASK OBJECTIVE	QUESTION	EXAMPLE	CRITERIA	COMMENT
IN 6	0 1 2 3 4 0 1 2 3 4 0 1 2 3 4 0 1 2 3 4	Prepares a list of questions to ask employer	Learner will prepare a list of questions to ask employer.	Can learner prepare a list of questions to ask employer?		4= prepares written list of at least 5 questions that learner might ask during interview and rehearses asking those questions out loud, 3= states at least 2 questions that learner might ask during interview and rehearses those questions out loud, 2= when given list of questions by caregiver, rehearses asking those questions out loud, 1= when given list of questions by caregiver, rehearses asking those questions out loud with only verbal prompts	
IN 7	0 1 2 3 4 0 1 2 3 4 0 1 2 3 4 0 1 2 3 4	Prepares to talk about strengths in relationship to the job	Learner will prepare to talk about strengths in relationship to the job.	Can learner prepare to talk about strengths in relationship to the job?		4= lists (verbally or in written form) at least 4 strengths or relevant job related skills and discusses those strengths with caregiver, 3= lists (verbally or in written form) at least 2 strengths or relevant job related skills and discusses those strengths with caregiver, 2= states at least 2 skills relevant to the position, 1= states 1 skill learner possesses relevant to position from list or with verbal prompts	
IN 8	0 1 2 0 1 2 0 1 2 0 1 2	Displays adequate hygiene for interview	Learner will display adequate hygiene at an interview.	Does learner display adequate hygiene for interview?	Hair clean and brushed/combed, teeth clean, does not have foul odor, fingernails clean and trimmed, freshly showered or clean, etc.	2= displays appropriate hygiene for interview, 1= displays appropriate hygiene for interview with verbal prompts as learner prepares for the interview	
IN 9	0 1 2 3 4 0 1 2 3 4 0 1 2 3 4 0 1 2 3 4	Answers variety of questions during mock interview	Learner will answer a variety of questions during a mock interview.	Does learner answer a variety of questions during a mock interview?		4= active listening, asks relevant questions, answers open-ended questions, 3= independently answers specific questions, asks relevant questions with only verbal prompts, 2= active listening and answers specific questions, 1= answers specific questions	
IN 10	0 1 2 0 1 2 0 1 2 0 1 2	Demonstrates "soft skills" during mock interview	Learner will demonstrate "soft skills" during mock interview.	Does learner demonstrate a variety of "soft skills" during mock interview so that appearance and interactions are relaxed and confident?	Handshake, eye contact on greeting, thank you at end of interview, good posture, takes notes, asks for clarification, smiles, makes appropriate "small talk," seems relaxed, good manners, positive affect, etc.	2= uses a variety of "soft skills" when answering questions and participating in mock interview so as to appear relaxed and confident, 1= appropriately greets and shakes hands with interviewer	

The AFLS® - Vocational Skills Protocol

The Assessment of Functional Living Skills - The AFLS®

Interview (Continued)

Participating in an interview

TASK	SCORE	TASK NAME	TASK OBJECTIVE	QUESTION	EXAMPLE	CRITERIA	COMMENT
IN 11	0 1 2 0 1 2 0 1 2 0 1 2	Dresses professionally	Learner will dress professionally for interview.	Can learner dress professionally for interview?		2= describes professional dress for learner's gender and dresses professionally for job interview, 1= dresses professionally for job interview with verbal prompts or assistance from caregiver	
IN 12	0 1 2 0 1 2 0 1 2 0 1 2	Describes relevant experience	Learner will describe relevant work experiences.	Can learner describe relevant work experiences?	So, tell me about your last job. Learner identifies job title, responsibilities, roles, company name, how long employed, etc.	2= describes past experiences to interviewer relevant for position sought in conversational manner, 1= describes past experiences only in response to direct questions from interviewer about specific experiences	
IN 13	0 1 2 0 1 2 0 1 2 0 1 2	Asks appropriate and relevant questions	Learner will ask appropriate and relevant questions during interview.	Can learner ask appropriate and relevant questions during interview?	Does the position include any paid holidays or sick time? Brings a written list of questions to ensure information is obtained during the interview	2= asks questions of interviewer relevant to gain position details, 1= asks questions when verbally prompted by caregiver or when using a predetermined list of questions	The use of text or picture prompts or gesturing to a written list by caregiver as a prompt should be scored a "1"
IN 14	0 1 2 0 1 2 0 1 2 0 1 2	Answers interview questions	Learner will answer questions in a conversational style.	Can learner answer interview questions in a conversational style?	Have you ever worked in a restaurant? Yes, I worked in a restaurant for 2 years cleaning tables	2= answers open-ended questions using multiple details relevant to experience, 1= answers closed-ended questions	
IN 15	0 1 2 3 4 0 1 2 3 4 0 1 2 3 4 0 1 2 3 4	Uses a communication device	Learner will use a communication device to communicate during interview.	Can learner use a communication device to communicate during interview?		4= uses a device that is set up and programmed to ask questions, answer open-ended questions, describe work experiences, and personal information, 3= uses a device that is set up and programmed to answer open-ended questions, describe previous work experiences, and personal information, 2= uses device that is set up and programmed to answer yes/no questions and provide personal information, 1= uses device set up and programmed to answer yes/no questions	Should be scored N/A if learner uses vocal communication as primary source

The AFLS® - Vocational Skills Protocol

The Assessment of Functional Living Skills - The AFLS®

Interview (Continued)

TASK	SCORE	TASK NAME	TASK OBJECTIVE	QUESTION	EXAMPLE	CRITERIA	COMMENT
IN 16	0 1 2 3 4 0 1 2 3 4 0 1 2 3 4 0 1 2 3 4	Pays attention during interview	Learner will pay attention during job interview.	Does learner pay attention during job interview?	Looks at interviewer, listens to interviewer and responds to questions, not distracted by office or setting; Active listening behavior includes nodding, "Um Hum," "yes," "I see," etc.	4= pays attention during job interview for more than 30 minutes when caregiver is not present and demonstrates active listening behaviors, 3= pays attention during job interview for 15 minutes when caregiver is not present and demonstrates active listening behaviors, 2= pays attention during job interview for more than 15 minutes when caregiver is present and providing only minimal and infrequent prompts, 1= pays attention during job interview for 10 minutes when caregiver is present and providing only minimal and infrequent prompts	
IN 17	0 1 2 0 1 2 0 1 2 0 1 2	Takes notes during interview	Learner will take notes during interview.	Does learner take notes during interview?	Notes would be taken on information not provided in want ad, job posting, or specific details of information more generally presented in job posting	2= takes notes on important information delivered at interview, and as necessary, asks interviewer to repeat oneself, to clarify, or wait a moment to ensure notes are taken, 1= takes notes on a few important pieces of information when verbally or gesturally prompted by caregiver	
IN 18	0 1 2 0 1 2 0 1 2 0 1 2	Determines benefits package of position during interview	Learner will determine benefits package of position during interview.	Does learner determine benefits package of position during interview?	Which holidays are paid? Does the position require shifts every Saturday? It says, "Competitive salary," what is the salary?	2= obtains details of benefits package by questioning interviewer, 1= obtains details of benefits package when verbally prompted by caregiver	Use of a written list of questions or other self prompting is acceptable for a score of 2
IN 19	0 1 2 0 1 2 0 1 2 0 1 2	Talks about concerns from past employers	Learner will talk about concerns of previous employers.	Can learner talk about concerns of previous employers?	While being honest, learner remains positive, does not disparage previous coworkers or employers, "spins" negative information into positive situation such as, "I was written up 3 times at my last job for being late. But, I bought a new alarm clock and have an apartment by the bus station and ever since, I've been on time."	2= when asked about concerns with previous work behavior, discusses new behavioral patterns that have replaced previous negative behaviors and discusses "work arounds" for potential issues, 1= admits that behaviors demonstrated at previous work site caused problems for employer	

The AFLS® - Vocational Skills Protocol

The Assessment of Functional Living Skills - The AFLS®

Interview (Continued)

TASK	SCORE	TASK NAME	TASK OBJECTIVE	QUESTION	EXAMPLE	CRITERIA	COMMENT
IN 20	0 1 2 0 1 2 0 1 2 0 1 2	Demonstrates "soft skills" during interview	Learner will demonstrate "soft skills" during interview.	Does learner demonstrate a variety of "soft skills" during mock interview so that appearance and interactions are relaxed and confident?	Handshake, eye contact on greeting, thank you at end of interview, good posture, takes notes, asks for clarification, smiles, makes appropriate "small talk," seems relaxed, good manners, positive affect, etc.	2= uses a variety of "soft skills" when answering questions and participating in interview so as to appear relaxed and confident, 1= appropriately greets and shakes hands with interviewer	
IN 21	0 1 2 3 4 0 1 2 3 4 0 1 2 3 4 0 1 2 3 4	Prepares a follow-up letter/thank you note	Learner will prepare and send a follow up letter/thank you note.	Can learner prepare and send a follow up letter/thank you note?	Contact possible employer immediately after interview, uses template found online to guide structure of letter, etc.	4= independently prepares and sends thank you letter, 3= provides all relevant information for follow-up letter, requires only verbal prompts to compose and write letter, 2= provides the content for letter but requires someone else to compose and type, 1= requires verbal prompts to generate content of letter	
IN 22	0 1 2 0 1 2 0 1 2 0 1 2	Responds to job offer and negotiates terms	Learner will respond to job offer and negotiate for different terms of position.	Can learner respond to job offer and negotiate for different terms for position?	More benefits, greater compensation, different hours than posted, etc.	2= prior to accepting or rejecting an offer for employment, negotiates to improve terms of position, 1= considers offer and if terms are satisfactory, accepts position, and clarifies start date	

The AFLS® - Vocational Skills Protocol

The Assessment of Functional Living Skills - The AFLS®

Basic Skills

Following directions and learning new skills

TASK	SCORE	TASK NAME	TASK OBJECTIVE	QUESTION	EXAMPLE	CRITERIA	COMMENT
BS 1	0 1 2 3 4 0 1 2 3 4 0 1 2 3 4 0 1 2 3 4	Follows simple verbal directions	Learner will follow simple verbal directions.	Does learner follow simple verbal directions?	Move box of shirts to counter, sort the shirts by size, take the empty box to the storage room, break down the box, and put it in the recycling pile	4= consistently follows 4-step directions, 3= consistently follows 3-step directions, 2= consistently follows 2-step directions, 1= consistently follows 2-step directions with only verbal prompts	
BS 2	0 1 2 3 4 0 1 2 3 4 0 1 2 3 4 0 1 2 3 4	Follows written directions	Learner will follow written directions.	Does learner follow written directions?		4= consistently follows 4-step directions, 3= consistently follows 3-step written directions, 2= consistently follows 2-step written directions, 1= consistently follows 1-step written directions	
BS 3	0 1 2 3 4 0 1 2 3 4 0 1 2 3 4 0 1 2 3 4	Pays attention during training	Learner will attend to instructor when learning new information.	Does learner attend to instructor when learning new information?	Instructor, supervisor, coach, teacher, etc. in group lecture, small group, or direct one-to-one instruction	4= attends to instructor for 30 minutes when there is at least a 1:4 instructor/trainee ratio, 3= attends to instructor for 15 minutes when there is at least a 1:3 instructor/trainee ratio, 2= attends to instructor for 15 minutes when there is at least a 1:2 instructor/trainee ratio, 1= attends to instructor for 15 minutes when there is a 1:1 instructor/trainee ratio	
BS 4	0 1 2 0 1 2 0 1 2 0 1 2	Confirms information	Learner will confirm information delivered by supervisor.	Does learner confirm information delivered by supervisor?		2= asks for clarification or for information to be repeated to confirm accuracy, 1= tells instructor when learner is confused or does not understand instructions	
BS 5	0 1 2 0 1 2 0 1 2 0 1 2	Learns new skills quickly	Learner will acquire new skills without intensive instruction.	Does learner acquire new skills without intensive instruction?	Stapling paper, stacking boxes, loading paper into a printer, transferring a phone call, change light bulb, etc.	2= learns most relatively simple skills after only 1 demonstration, 1= learns relatively simple skills after shown a demonstration of the skill less than 5 times	
BS 6	0 1 2 3 4 0 1 2 3 4 0 1 2 3 4 0 1 2 3 4	Focuses on specific job task	Learner will focus on specific job task for at least 45 minutes.	Does learner focus on a specific task for at least 45 minutes?	Assembling informational folders, welding, stocking shelves, entering computer code for new website, editing videos, etc.	4= remains focused and attentive to task for up to 45 minutes, 3= remains focused and attentive to task for up to 30 minutes, 2= remains focused and attentive to task for at least 15 minutes, 1= remains focused and attentive to task for at least 5 minutes	Focus on task should be scored even if learner briefly looks away or diverts attention for small periods without any "major" departure from task

The AFLS® - Vocational Skills Protocol

The Assessment of Functional Living Skills - The AFLS®

Basic Skills (Continued)

TASK	SCORE	TASK NAME	TASK OBJECTIVE	QUESTION	EXAMPLE	CRITERIA	COMMENT
BS 7	0 1 2 0 1 2 0 1 2 0 1 2	Performs non-preferred tasks	Learner will state that even though not all tasks are pleasant, they still need to be done, and completes the tasks without significant complaining.	Does learner do unpleasant or non-preferred tasks that need to be done?	Doesn't like to stack boxes, but knows it is part of the job, doesn't like to clean the toilet, but does it anyway, etc.	2= completes non-preferred tasks without significant complaining, 1= requires only verbal prompts to do non-preferred tasks	
BS 8	0 1 2 0 1 2 0 1 2 0 1 2	Performs all assigned tasks during shift	Learner will perform assigned tasks throughout shift.	Does learner consistently complete all assigned job tasks within a shift?	Stocks vegetables in produce department, every 45 minutes checks vegetables to ensure they are moist, replaces rolls of plastic vegetable bags, sweeps floor of produce area, scans and romaine lettuce and tears off withered leaves to keep fresh look, etc.	2= independently and consistently performs all job tasks and expectations throughout shift, 1= requires occasional verbal prompts to ensure all job tasks are completed	When scoring this item, accommodations such as visual schedules that are utilized independently by the learner are not considered prompts
BS 9	0 1 2 0 1 2 0 1 2 0 1 2	Adjusts priorities during work	Learner will adjust momentary work activities to respond to sudden changes in job priorities.	Does learner adjust momentary work activities to respond to sudden changes in job priorities?	Folding clothes and placing on display shelf when customer spills drink on the floor, learner stops folding clothes, retrieves cleaning materials and cleans floor before returning to folding clothes	2= while performing assigned tasks, notices an issue that requires immediate action, independently shifts activities and addresses the issue, 1= while performing assigned tasks, notices an issue that requires immediate action, addresses the issue when directed to by supervisor	
BS 10	0 1 2 0 1 2 0 1 2 0 1 2	Completes end of shift duties	Learner will complete end of shift routine prior to leaving job site.	Does learner complete end of shift routine prior to leaving job site?	Finishes assigned task prior to leaving, notifies supervisor when leaving, waits for replacement to show up, put materials or equipment away, etc.	2= consistently completes expected end of shift routine prior to leaving job site, 1= completes expected end of shift routine prior to leaving job site with only verbal prompts	

The AFLS® - Vocational Skills Protocol

The Assessment of Functional Living Skills - The AFLS®

Basic Skills (Continued)

Dependability

TASK	SCORE	TASK NAME	TASK OBJECTIVE	QUESTION	EXAMPLE	CRITERIA	COMMENT
BS 11	1 1 2 0 1 2 0 1 2 0 1 2	Arranges or has reliable transportation	Learner will use their own or arrange reliable transportation to get to job site.	Does learner have or do they arrange a mode of transportation to get to job site?	Reliable transportation include learner's own operational vehicle, walking distance, biking distance, living within walking distance to public transportation that drops close to job site, etc. Unreliable transportation includes a friend driving learner to work every day, vehicle with consistent mechanical issues, etc.	2= uses own reliable means or transportation or uses a reliable means of transportation, 1= uses an inconsistent means of transportation or one that is outside the learner's control	
BS 12	0 1 2 0 1 2 0 1 2 0 1 2	Demonstrates consistent attendance	Learner will consistently attend job.	Does learner consistently attend work?		2= only misses work for illnesses at a rate consistent with coworkers, 1= misses work no more than twice a month	
BS 13	0 1 2 0 1 2 0 1 2 0 1 2	Demonstrates punctual arrival and departure	Learner will arrive and depart work on time.	Does learner arrive and depart work on time?		2= consistently arrives early or on time for work **and** consistently stays for entire shift, 1= consistently arrives early or on time for work **or** consistently stays for entire shift	
BS 14	0 1 2 0 1 2 0 1 2 0 1 2	Notifies employer when work will be missed or when learner will be late	Learner will notify employer when work will be missed or when learner will be late.	Does learner notify employer when work will be missed or when learner will be late?	Method of notification can include call, email, or text message depending on the expectations of the position	2= consistently notifies employer in a timely manner every time work will be missed, when learner will be late, and resolves the issue that was causing the missed or late shifts (if possible), 1= notifies employer prior to the start of the assigned shift when work will be missed	
BS 15	0 1 2 0 1 2 0 1 2 0 1 2	Remains calm at work	Learner will remain calm at work.	Does learner remain calm at work?	Reacts calmly when someone borrowed learner's pencil from desk without asking, supervisor edits written report and points out mistakes, etc.	2= consistently reacts appropriately, calmly, or as is typical given the situation, 1= reacts inappropriately or in a disruptive manner no more than once per week	

The AFLS® - Vocational Skills Protocol

The Assessment of Functional Living Skills - The AFLS®

Basic Skills (Continued)

TASK	SCORE	TASK NAME	TASK OBJECTIVE	QUESTION	EXAMPLE	CRITERIA	COMMENT
BS 16	0 1 2 0 1 2 0 1 2 0 1 2	Demonstrates non-disruptive behavior in work environment	Learner will demonstrate non-disruptive behavior while at work.	Does learner demonstrate disruptive behavior while at work?	Listening to music, loud talking, bothering others who are working	2= never disrupts work environment, 1= requires occasional reminders to correct disruptive behavior while working	
BS 17	0 1 2 0 1 2 0 1 2 0 1 2	Displays trustworthiness	Learner will not steal or lie at work.	Does learner steal or lie at work?	"White" lies to avoid insulting someone or to save someone from embarrassment should be acceptable when scoring this item	2= is truthful with employers and fellow employees and does not steal, 1= does not steal while at work	
BS 18	0 1 2 0 1 2 0 1 2 0 1 2	Seeks new assignments	Learner will notify supervisor when task is completed and ask for new assignment.	Does learner notify supervisor when task is completed and ask for new assignment?	While learner is collating and stapling handouts, supervisor approaches and instructs learner to notify him when task is finished, learner finishes stacking shirts on display and goes to supervisor to ask for next assignment	2= notifies supervisor when assigned task is completed and asks for next assignment, 1= when nearing the end of a task and instructed to inform supervisor when finished, notifies supervisor upon completion	
BS 19	0 1 2 0 1 2 0 1 2 0 1 2	Job or task planning	When assigned a project, learner will plan for necessary sequence of steps to complete tasks and perform the actions required to complete task.	Can learner formulate a plan to carry out a sequence of steps required to complete job or task?	Complex tasks: Design an announcement or marketing brochure, set up a room for a party or event, plans wiring for basement renovation, organizes sequence of activities for lawn maintenance crew, etc. Simple tasks: Mow lawn, restock shelves, clean up after construction crew, clean a restroom, etc.	2= plans and performs necessary sequence of steps to complete complex tasks, 1= plans and performs necessary sequence of steps to complete simple tasks	
BS 20	0 1 2 0 1 2 0 1 2 0 1 2	Maintains speed of process	Learner will maintain speed of process.	Can learner maintain speed of process?		2= maintains expected speed on job role, 1= requires occasional reminders to maintain expected pace	

The AFLS® - Vocational Skills Protocol

The Assessment of Functional Living Skills - The AFLS®

Basic Skills (Continued)

Cleanliness and personal management

TASK	SCORE	TASK NAME	TASK OBJECTIVE	QUESTION	EXAMPLE	CRITERIA	COMMENT
BS 21	0 1 2 0 1 2 0 1 2 0 1 2	Solves problems to overcome barriers to task completion	When learner comes into contact with obstacles or barriers to task completion, learner will identify work arounds, alternative solutions, or change original plan to achieve intended outcome.	Does learner identify work arounds, alternative solutions, or change original plan to achieve intended outcome?	When told to sweep floor, dustpan cannot be located, uses flap of cardboard box as dustpan, When thermostat needs to be adjusted but is locked, learner seeks office manager to obtain key to unlock thermostat and change temperature, When cleaning the bathroom mirrors, learner runs out of paper towels and uses toilet paper to finish cleaning the final mirror, etc.	2= consistently identifies solutions and workarounds to overcome obstacles when faced with problems during tasks, 1= notifies supervisor when faced with obstacle during work, requires assistance from supervisor to identify solutions or workarounds to overcome that obstacle	
BS 22	0 1 2 0 1 2 0 1 2 0 1 2	Wears clothing appropriate for job	Learner will wear clothing appropriate for job.	Does learner wear clothing appropriate for job?	Professional dress and neat clothing appearance for positions in which this is expected, avoids offensive slogans or inappropriate pictures on clothes, appropriate footwear to include safety issues and weather conditions, etc.	2= always dresses appropriately for position, 1= requires occasional reminders to dress appropriately for position	
BS 23	0 1 2 0 1 2 0 1 2 0 1 2	Maintains adequate hygiene at job	Learner will maintain adequate hygiene while at work.	Does learner maintain adequate hygiene at work?	Hair clean and brushed/combed, teeth clean, does not have foul odor, fingernails clean and trimmed, freshly showered or clean, etc.	2= always maintains appropriate hygiene for work, 1= maintains appropriate hygiene at least half of all work days	
BS 24	0 1 2 0 1 2 0 1 2 0 1 2	Keeps self and clothing clean when performing tasks	Learner will keeps self and clothing clean when performing work tasks.	Does learner keep self and clothing clean when performing work tasks?	Handling oils, food items, ink cartridges, etc. unless unavoidable in positions such as gardening, warehouse work, construction, etc.	2= consistently keeps self clean or immediately cleans self or clothing, 1= requires verbal reminders to stay clean	
BS 25	0 1 2 0 1 2 0 1 2 0 1 2	Adjusts clothing when changing tasks	Learner will adjust clothing when changing tasks.	Does learner adjust clothing when changing tasks?	Puts on boots and coat when going outside, etc.	2= consistently changes or adjusts clothing when needed, 1= requires verbal reminders to change or adjust clothing	

The Assessment of Functional Living Skills - The AFLS®

Basic Skills (Continued)

TASK	SCORE	TASK NAME	TASK OBJECTIVE	QUESTION	EXAMPLE	CRITERIA	COMMENT
BS 26	0 1 2 0 1 2 0 1 2 0 1 2	Maintains a clean and tidy work area	Learner will maintain a clean and tidy work area.	Does learner maintain a clean and tidy work area?		2= consistently keeps work area and personal belongings clean and tidy, 1= requires verbal prompts to keep area clean and tidy	
BS 27	0 1 2 0 1 2 0 1 2 0 1 2	Storage of personal possessions	Learner will store personal possessions in a secure location.	Does learner store personal possessions in secure location?	Puts purse in secure locker when arrives at work	2= stores personal belongings in locked personal locker, safe location approved for personal storage of items, or arranges temporary storage when items are not typically brought to work, 1= stores personal belongings in safe location only with verbal reminders	

Dealing with problem situations

TASK	SCORE	TASK NAME	TASK OBJECTIVE	QUESTION	EXAMPLE	CRITERIA	COMMENT
BS 28	0 1 2 0 1 2 0 1 2 0 1 2	Requests accommodation to deal with sensory issues	Learner will request accommodations to deal with sensory issues.	Does learner request accommodations to deal with sensory issues?	Lighting, noise, smells, etc.	2= identifies potential solutions to problematic situations and seeks approval from supervisor for accommodations, 1= reports problematic situations to supervisor and asks for help in finding accommodations	
BS 29	0 1 2 0 1 2 0 1 2 0 1 2	Attends to minor injuries	Learner will attend to minor injuries.	Does learner attend to minor injuries?	Something in eye, cut, scrape, minor burns, splinter, bump on head, etc.	2= remains calm when injured and applies common first-aid to minor injuries, 1= locates first-aid kit and applies bandage to small cut	NEEDS CLOSE SUPERVISION
BS 30	0 1 2 0 1 2 0 1 2 0 1 2	Over the counter medication	Learner will use over the counter medication in appropriate manner when needed.	Does learner use over the counter medication?	Stomach ache, head ache, tooth ache, sore muscles, cramps, etc.	2= states location of medication and describes the symptoms treated and correct dosage for 4 different over the counter medications, 1= states which over the counter medication is taken for at least 2 symptoms	NEEDS CLOSE SUPERVISION
BS 31	0 1 2 0 1 2 0 1 2 0 1 2	Notifies supervisor of injury	Learner will state what actions to take and which reporting procedures to follow for various job-related injuries.	Does learner know what to do in case of job-related injuries?	States that when leg is bruised or a finger is slightly cut, supervisor does not need to be notified, box falls from shelf and hits learner in head, reports accident to supervisor, etc.	2= states actions to take and reporting procedures to follow for various job-related injuries, 1= states which injuries need to be reported to supervisor	NEEDS CLOSE SUPERVISION

The AFLS® - Vocational Skills Protocol

The Assessment of Functional Living Skills - The AFLS®

Basic Skills (Continued)

TASK	SCORE	TASK NAME	TASK OBJECTIVE	QUESTION	EXAMPLE	CRITERIA	COMMENT
BS 32	0 1 2 0 1 2 0 1 2 0 1 2	Admits mistakes	Learner will recognize when mistakes are made and notify supervisor.	Does learner notify supervisor about mistakes?	Forgets to send package, realizes mistake and sends the package the next day, sent package to billing rather than shipping address and notifies supervisor so customer can be contacted, etc.	2= recognizes and self-corrects mistake if possible, if not possible, voluntarily notifies supervisor to inform about mistake, 1=acknowledges their action when asked if they did something that unknowingly or inadvertently caused a problem	

Forms and following of work protocol

TASK	SCORE	TASK NAME	TASK OBJECTIVE	QUESTION	EXAMPLE	CRITERIA	COMMENT
BS 33	0 1 2 0 1 2 0 1 2 0 1 2	Carries personal identification or name badge	Learner will carry an personal identification or wear a name badge.	Does learner carry personal identification or wear a name badge?	If name badge is required for position, score item using name badge regardless of carrying other forms of personal identification	2= always wears name badge or carries personal identification, 1= requires occasional reminders to wear name badge or carry personal identification	
BS 34	0 1 2 0 1 2 0 1 2 0 1 2	Fills out attendance forms	Learner will fill out attendance forms.	Does learner fill out attendance forms?		2= consistently completes attendance form and submits by required time, 1= independently completes attendance form, requires verbal prompts to consistently meet timelines	
BS 35	0 1 2 0 1 2 0 1 2 0 1 2	Operates a time clock	Learner will operate time clock.	Does learner operate time clock?		2= consistently uses time clock to clock in and out from work on daily basis, 1= clocks in and out with verbal prompts or reminders	
BS 36	0 1 2 0 1 2 0 1 2 0 1 2	Requests time off	Learner will request time off prior to taking off time from work.	Does learner follow company procedures to request time off?		2= requests time off from work with adequate notice by completing forms or other procedures required by the company, 1= asks employer or supervisor for permission to miss days, requires verbal assistance to use forms	
BS 37	0 1 2 3 4 0 1 2 3 4 0 1 2 3 4 0 1 2 3 4	Reads paystubs	Learner will explain the different amounts of earnings and withholdings shown on paystubs.	Can learner explain the different amounts of earnings and withholdings shown on paystub?	Federal taxes, state taxes, Medicaid, FICA, 401K or other retirement plan, etc.	4= states gross and net earnings and amounts and reasons for all withholdings, 3= explains meaning of gross, net, and taxes, 2= explains difference between gross and net pay, 1= can identify net pay amount on pay check stub	

The AFLS® - Vocational Skills Protocol

The Assessment of Functional Living Skills - The AFLS®

Basic Skills (Continued)

Social interaction issues

TASK	SCORE	TASK NAME	TASK OBJECTIVE	QUESTION	EXAMPLE	CRITERIA	COMMENT
BS 38	0 1 2 0 1 2 0 1 2 0 1 2	Greets other employees	Learner will greet other employees.	Does learner greet other employees?	This item can be scored using AAC device, card exchange, or non-vocal sign. If it is, note which method is used in the comment column	2= initiates and returns greetings of coworkers, 1= returns greetings of coworkers	
BS 39	0 1 2 0 1 2 0 1 2 0 1 2	Shakes hands	Learner will offer and accept handshakes from others for an appropriate duration and using an appropriate grip.	Does learner look at others as giving a good handshake?	Looks at a person and gives a firm handshake for an appropriate amount of time, doesn't give a "too hard," "too soft," or "too exaggerated" handshake	2= offers to shake hand when socially appropriate and shakes with appropriate grip for reasonable amount of time, 1= accepts person's offer to shake hand	
BS 40	0 1 2 0 1 2 0 1 2 0 1 2	Demonstrates eye contact when talking with others	Learner will use appropriate eye contact when talking with others.	Does learner use appropriate eye contact when talking with others?		2= maintains eye contact in manner consistent with cultural norms, 1= remains physically oriented to speaker but requires verbal prompts to maintain eye contact	
BS 41	0 1 2 0 1 2 0 1 2 0 1 2	Interacts with others in a friendly and courteous interaction style	Learner will interact with others in a friendly and courteous interaction style.	Does learner interact with others in a friendly and courteous interaction style?		2= uses friendly and courteous interaction style with everyone, 1= uses friendly and courteous interaction style with people that learner knows	
BS 42	0 1 2 0 1 2 0 1 2 0 1 2	Takes breaks	Learner will notify supervisor prior to taking a break and return from break on time.	Does learner notify supervisor prior to taking a break and return from break on time?		2= notifies supervisor prior to taking a break and returns from break on time, 1= returns from break on time	
BS 43	0 1 2 0 1 2 0 1 2 0 1 2	Break room etiquette	Learner will abide by accepted guidelines and rules in break room.	Does learner abide by guidelines and rules in break room?	Only eats food brought by learner, cleans out food left in refrigerator by learner, use of electronic devices, etc.	2= demonstrates appropriate behavior and follows local norms and rules when in break room, 1= requires occasional reminders from supervisor or coworkers regarding rules or norms of break room	
BS 44	0 1 2 0 1 2 0 1 2 0 1 2	Respects personal space of others	Learner will respect the personal space of others.	Does learner respect the personal space of others?	Personal space is different given different activities, settings, and with whom the learner is interacting	2= respects the personal space of others, maintains acceptable space between others unless closer space is required for work activities, 1= requires occasional reminders to respect others' personal space	

The AFLS® - Vocational Skills Protocol

The Assessment of Functional Living Skills - The AFLS®

Coworker Relations

Workplace hierarchy

TASK	SCORE	TASK NAME	TASK OBJECTIVE	QUESTION	EXAMPLE	CRITERIA	COMMENT
CR 1	0 1 2 0 1 2 0 1 2 0 1 2	Identifies supervisor	Learner will identify supervisor(s).	Can learner identify supervisor(s)?	If learner has more than one direct supervisor, each needs to be identified for scoring this item	2= states name of supervisor(s), 1= receptively identifies supervisor(s),	
CR 2	0 1 2 3 4 0 1 2 3 4 0 1 2 3 4 0 1 2 3 4	States staff hierarchy	Learner will state staff hierarchy.	Can learner state staff hierarchy?	Coworker in cubicle next to learner talks loudly on the phone, learner tells immediate supervisor and refrains from emailing the owner of the company, etc.	4= states at least 3 people "above" learner in the correct order of level or power, states at least 2 others on the same level or that share equal power, respects hierarchy by not "going around" immediate supervisors, 3= states 2 people "above" learner in the correct order of level or power, states at least 1 other on the same level or that share equal power, 2= states 3 other coworkers including immediate supervisor, 1= states name of 1 coworker	
CR 3	0 1 2 0 1 2 0 1 2 0 1 2	Follows directives from supervisors or others when reasonable or beneficial to task	Learner will follow directions from supervisors and from others when reasonable.	Does learner follow directions from appropriate people?	While learner is raking leaves into a pile, a coworker tells him to stack wood in the back of the house, learner tells coworker he needs to finish raking leaves, while learner is raking leaves into a pile, a coworker asks him to help drag a heavy log into the woods in the back of the house, learner helps coworker and then finishes raking leaves	2= follows directions from supervisor or other reasonable directions from coworkers that are beneficial to task or to the team, without neglecting assigned task, 1= follows directions from 1 specific supervisor and gets approval before changing tasks requested by coworker	
CR 4	0 1 2 0 1 2 0 1 2 0 1 2	Describes role of coworkers	Learner will describe the various roles of coworkers.	Can learner describe the various roles of coworkers?		2= describes roles of at least 4 coworkers, 1= describes the role of at least 2 coworkers	

The AFLS® - Vocational Skills Protocol

The Assessment of Functional Living Skills - The AFLS®

Coworker Relations (Continued)

TASK	SCORE	TASK NAME	TASK OBJECTIVE	QUESTION	EXAMPLE	CRITERIA	COMMENT
CR 5	0 1 2 0 1 2 0 1 2 0 1 2	Describes work culture	Learner will describe the work culture at a particular job site.	Can learner describe the work culture at a particular job site?	Work culture is the values, beliefs, and expectation of a company or workplace and includes practical things such as when to talk, when not to talk, what is acceptable to do and not do, noise level, professionalism, personal expression, breaks, discipline, seriousness, work ethic, etc.	2= describes the work culture accurately, 1= requires verbal assistance to fully describe culture	

Common social workplace interactions

TASK	SCORE	TASK NAME	TASK OBJECTIVE	QUESTION	EXAMPLE	CRITERIA	COMMENT
CR 6	0 1 2 3 4 0 1 2 3 4 0 1 2 3 4 0 1 2 3 4	Uses appropriate topics of conversation for work environment	Learner will discuss only appropriate topics of conversation for the work environment.	Does learner discuss only appropriate topics of conversation for the work environment?	Racial, sexual, gross, violent, overly religious, drug or alcohol related, etc.	4= states at least 4 "safe" topics of conversation and at least 4 topics that should be avoided at work and maintains appropriate topics of conversation at work, 3= states at least 4 "safe" topics of conversation and at least 2 topics that should be avoided at work, 2= states at least 4 "safe" topics of conversation, 1= states at least 2 safe topics of conversation at work	
CR 7	0 1 2 0 1 2 0 1 2 0 1 2	Demonstrates small talk with coworkers and boss	Learner will converse and make "small talk" with coworkers and boss.	Does learner converse and make "small talk" with coworkers and boss?		2= makes casual conversation with coworkers and supervisors of appropriate content and during appropriate times that do not interfere with performance, 1= makes conversation and small talk with coworkers at appropriate times and of appropriate content	

More difficult workplace interactions

TASK	SCORE	TASK NAME	TASK OBJECTIVE	QUESTION	EXAMPLE	CRITERIA	COMMENT
CR 8	0 1 2 0 1 2 0 1 2 0 1 2	Knows when appropriate to talk about others' behavior	Learner will know when it is appropriate to talk about others' behavior.	Does learner know when it is appropriate to talk about others' behavior?	When work of others is causing difficulty in doing the job; When not to: breaking minor rules, not working, making errors, lack of perfection, etc.	2= states when it is and is not appropriate to talk about the behavior of others, 1= states when it is inappropriate to talk about the behavior of others	

The AFLS® - Vocational Skills Protocol

The Assessment of Functional Living Skills - The AFLS®

Coworker Relations (Continued)

TASK	SCORE	TASK NAME	TASK OBJECTIVE	QUESTION	EXAMPLE	CRITERIA	COMMENT
CR 9	0 1 2 0 1 2 0 1 2 0 1 2	Avoids workplace drama	Learner will keep out of others' personal and workplace issues.	Does learner keep out of others' personal and workplace issues?	Learner walks into break room as 2 coworkers are discussing another employee, learner turns and walks away, keeps comments about others positive or constructive in nature, etc.	2= avoids workplace drama and does not get involved in other's affairs (without being directly asked to do so), 1= needs occasional reminders to not get involved in others' personal or workplace issues	
CR 10	0 1 2 0 1 2 0 1 2 0 1 2	Demonstrates assertiveness when appropriate	Learner will be assertive when appropriate in work-related conflicts.	Is learner assertive when appropriate in work-related conflicts?	Learner overhears a coworker telling someone a lie about her, learner corrects the coworker by explaining what actually happened	2= sticks up for self in times of personal or work related conflict in a calm but direct manner, 1= sticks up for self in personal or work-related conflict, requires verbal prompts to remain calm	NEEDS CLOSE SUPERVISION
CR 11	0 1 2 0 1 2 0 1 2 0 1 2	Responds appropriately to bullying	Learner will respond by seeking appropriate assistance when being "bullied."	Does learner understand "bullying" and respond appropriately?	When coworkers make aggressive or hurtful comments, attempt to get learner to do something learner does not want to do, or a job directive that learner is not required to do, seeks assistance from authority figure, etc.	2= appropriately identifies (does not over-identify or mis-identify) when others are "bullying" and seeks assistance from authority figure, 1= identifies "bullying" situations, tries to avoid encounters, but requires assistance to identify appropriate actions to take to prevent or to stop the encounters	NEEDS CLOSE SUPERVISION
CR 12	0 1 2 0 1 2 0 1 2 0 1 2	Walks away from confrontations	Learner will walk away physically remove self from an individual who is being inappropriately confrontative and may pose a physical threat.	Does learner identify that for personal safety it is sometimes necessary to physically walk away from someone who is being confrontative?	Walks away from a hostile person trying to get learner to take responsibility for something someone else did	2= walks away or removes self from actual or potentially physical confrontations, 1= states the need to walk away or physically remove self from individuals who are acting in a manner such as to pose a physical threat	NEEDS CLOSE SUPERVISION

The AFLS® - Vocational Skills Protocol

The Assessment of Functional Living Skills - The AFLS®

Coworker Relations (Continued)

TASK	SCORE	TASK NAME	TASK OBJECTIVE	QUESTION	EXAMPLE	CRITERIA	COMMENT
CR 13	0 1 2 3 4 0 1 2 3 4 0 1 2 3 4 0 1 2 3 4	Receives suggestions and corrective feedback	Learner will respond in a calm manner when provided with suggestions or corrective feedback.	Does learner respond in a calm manner when provided with suggestions or corrective feedback?	Doesn't overreact when given corrective feedback	4= remains calm when receiving suggestions and corrective feedback, evaluates the information, and demonstrates incorporation of that feedback in similar situations in the future, 3= remains calm and requires only verbal prompts to consider changes in actions, 2= remains calm when provided with corrective feedback and suggestions, 1= **when presented very carefully,** remains calm when provided with corrective feedback and suggestions	
CR 14	0 1 2 0 1 2 0 1 2 0 1 2	Offers suggestions	Learner will offer suggestions to others to possibly improve a situation in a tactful manner.	Does learner offer suggestions in a tactful manner?		2= offers suggestions to others to possibly improve a situation in a tactful manner, 1= when ways of presenting suggestions are discussed beforehand, offers suggestions to others to possibly improve a situation in a tactful manner	
CR 15	0 1 2 3 4 0 1 2 3 4 0 1 2 3 4 0 1 2 3 4	Uses conflict resolution strategies	Learner will describe and use conflict resolution strategies.	Can learner describe and use conflict resolution strategies?	Walking away, calmly discussing other's point of view, clarifying role in the conflict, tell supervisor, mediate, etc.	4= states and uses 3 conflict resolution strategies in the workplace, 3= states and uses 2 strategies, 2= states and uses at least 1 strategy, 1= states 1 strategy but requires verbal prompts to use it in the work place to resolve conflicts	NEEDS CLOSE SUPERVISION

The AFLS® - Vocational Skills Protocol

The Assessment of Functional Living Skills - The AFLS®

Workplace Safety

Fall prevention

TASK	SCORE	TASK NAME	TASK OBJECTIVE	QUESTION	EXAMPLE	CRITERIA	COMMENT
WS 1	0 1 2 3 4 0 1 2 3 4 0 1 2 3 4 0 1 2 3 4	Identifies hazard or danger signs	Learner will identify hazard or danger signs.	Can learner identify hazard or danger signs?	Biohazard, high voltage, radioactive, non-potable water, pesticides and insecticides, construction work being done overhead, etc.	4= expressively and receptively identifies at least 10 signs, 3= receptively identifies 10 signs and expressively identifies 5 signs, 2= receptively identifies at least 10 signs, 1= receptively identifies at least 5 signs	**Warning:** All of the skills listed in this Workplace Safety section require close supervision until the learner demonstrates competence with each of these skills.
WS 2	0 1 2 0 1 2 0 1 2 0 1 2	Avoids dangers related to spills/wet surfaces	Learner will recognize dangers related to spills or wet surfaces and will walk carefully to avoid slipping or falling.	Does learner avoid dangers related to spills or wet surfaces?	Loading dock is wet from rain and learner is careful when loading truck, janitor is mopping floor, learner walks on dry part next to mopped area to get around it, etc.	2= avoids walking through or making contact with wet floors and surfaces when possible, and walks carefully through wet surfaces when necessary, 1= avoids walking through wet floors that are marked as such, but requires verbal prompts to avoid wet surfaces or unmarked wet floors	NEEDS CLOSE SUPERVISION
WS 3	0 1 2 0 1 2 0 1 2 0 1 2	Avoids dangers related to clutter	Learner will walk safely around both large and small scattered objects.	Does learner avoid dangers related to clutter?		2= walks safely around both large and small scattered objects, 1= walks safely around large objects	
WS 4	0 1 2 3 4 0 1 2 3 4 0 1 2 3 4 0 1 2 3 4	Uses ladders and stepstools	Learner will avoid dangers related to ladders and stepstools.	Does learner avoid dangers related to ladders a stepstools?	Complex tasks include taping areas to be painted, painting, cleaning gutters, etc. Simple tasks include changing light bulb, placing or retrieving a box from a high shelf, etc.	4= opens and closes all types of ladders and stepstools, ensures ladders are stable, requests someone to hold ladder if unstable, refrains from standing on top rung, moves ladder as needed to avoid unsafe reaching, climbs ladders and step stools with objects needed for job tasks, and safely performs complex job tasks while on ladder, 3= opens and closes all types of ladders and stepstools, ensures ladders are stable, refrains from standing on top rung, climbs ladders and stepstools with objects needed for job tasks, and performs simple job tasks while on ladder, 2= when ladders are opened and placed by others climbs to highest safe step while carrying objects, 1= when ladders are opened and placed by others climbs to 2 steps without carrying objects	NEEDS CLOSE SUPERVISION

The AFLS® - Vocational Skills Protocol

The Assessment of Functional Living Skills - The AFLS®

Workplace Safety (Continued)

TASK	SCORE	TASK NAME	TASK OBJECTIVE	QUESTION	EXAMPLE	CRITERIA	COMMENT
WS 5	0 1 2 0 1 2 0 1 2 0 1 2	Avoids dangers related to falling from a high location	Learner will avoid dangers related to falling from a high location.	Does learner avoid dangers related to falling from a high location?	Wears a safety harness when on a roof, stands back from the edge of a loading dock, etc.	2= takes appropriate precautions and safety steps when working by a ledge, a roof, or other setting in which learner could fall, 1= follows directions to use appropriate safety precautions related to potential falls	NEEDS CLOSE SUPERVISION

Hazards related to touching

TASK	SCORE	TASK NAME	TASK OBJECTIVE	QUESTION	EXAMPLE	CRITERIA	COMMENT
WS 6	0 1 2 0 1 2 0 1 2 0 1 2	Avoids dangers related to knives or other sharp objects	Learner will avoid dangers related to knives or other sharp objects.	Does learner avoid dangers related to knives and other sharp objects?	Cuts with blade of knife moving away from self, carries knives with blades pointing down, etc.	2= consistently handles knives and sharp objects without any safety concerns, 1= safely accepts and passes sharp knife and other sharp items to others and carries sharp knives by handle with blade down and away from body	NEEDS CLOSE SUPERVISION
WS 7	0 1 2 0 1 2 0 1 2 0 1 2	Avoids dangers related to hot items	Learner will avoid dangers related to hot items.	Does learner avoid dangers related to hot items?	Boiling water, cooking equipment, steam, welding or blow torch, etc.	2= demonstrates care around hot items and handles hot items safely, 1= identifies actual and potentially hot items and handles hot items safely with supervision	NEEDS CLOSE SUPERVISION
WS 8	0 1 2 0 1 2 0 1 2 0 1 2	Avoids dangers related to working in cold weather	Learner will avoid dangers related to working in cold weather.	Does learner avoid dangers related to working in cold weather?	Knows that wet hands can stick to frozen surfaces, frostbite, dresses in layers and wears gloves and a hat, etc.	2= dresses appropriately when working in cold weather and takes breaks indoors if getting too cold, 1= dresses appropriately for cold weather with only verbal prompts	NEEDS CLOSE SUPERVISION
WS 9	0 1 2 0 1 2 0 1 2 0 1 2	Avoids dangers related to broken glass	Learner will avoid dangers related to broken glass.	Does learner avoid dangers related to broken glass?		2= demonstrates care around and when cleaning broken glass, 1= demonstrates care around broken glass, requires verbal prompts when cleaning broken glass	NEEDS CLOSE SUPERVISION
WS 10	0 1 2 0 1 2 0 1 2 0 1 2	Avoids dangers related to harmful and toxic substances	Learner will avoid dangers related to harmful and toxic substances.	Does learner avoid dangers related to harmful and toxic substances?	Aerosol spray, paint, WD40, pesticides, cleaning products, etc. Puts on gloves when distributing pesticides in garden, stays upwind when spraying aerosol cans outside, etc.	2= avoids contact with harmful substances, washes skin if contact occurs, and safely transports or disposes of toxic substances , 1= avoids contact with toxic and harmful substances and safely handles those substances under close supervision	NEEDS CLOSE SUPERVISION

The AFLS® - Vocational Skills Protocol

The Assessment of Functional Living Skills - The AFLS®

Workplace Safety (Continued)

Identification of various hazards

TASK	SCORE	TASK NAME	TASK OBJECTIVE	QUESTION	EXAMPLE	CRITERIA	COMMENT
WS 11	0 1 2 0 1 2 0 1 2 0 1 2	Wears particle mask	Learner will wear particle mask to avoid dangers related to dirt, dust, or particles.	Does learner avoid dangers related to dirt, dust, or particles, requiring mask?		2= states conditions for which mask is required and uses a mask when needed, 1= wears a mask when directed to do so	NEEDS CLOSE SUPERVISION
WS 12	0 1 2 0 1 2 0 1 2 0 1 2	Wears respirator	Learner will recognize situations that require a respirator and will wear one as needed.	Does learner recognize situations that require a respirator and wear one as needed?	Before working around asbestos, fiberglass insulation, etc.	2= identifies situations that require a respirator and uses as needed, 1= uses respirator when told to do so	NEEDS CLOSE SUPERVISION
WS 13	0 1 2 0 1 2 0 1 2 0 1 2	Safely handles gasoline	Learner will avoid dangers related to gasoline.	Does learner safely handle gasoline?	Pumps gasoline into approved container while container is on the ground, uses a funnel when filling machines, uses in well ventilated areas, does not inhale fumes, keep away from flames and sources of ignition, etc.	2= safely handles gasoline, 1= safely handles gasoline with close supervision	NEEDS CLOSE SUPERVISION
WS 14	0 1 2 0 1 2 0 1 2 0 1 2	Avoids dangers related to fumes that should be vented	Learner will avoid dangers related to fumes that should be vented.	Does learner avoid dangers related to fumes that should be vented?	Opens windows or doors prior to using items that may smoke or contain fumes from gasoline, pesticides, paint, etc.	2= takes reasonable precautions prior to creating fumes to avoid injury, moves away from areas containing fumes when ventilation is poor and diffuses fumes by opening doors or windows or turning on a fan, etc., 1= notifies supervisor and coworkers when fumes are present, complies when told to leave area because fumes are present	NEEDS CLOSE SUPERVISION
WS 15	0 1 2 0 1 2 0 1 2 0 1 2	Safely places objects to avoid risk of those objects falling	Learner will safely place objects so as to minimize the hazard of falling objects.	Does learner safely place objects so as to minimize the hazard of falling objects?	Boxes on top of shelves	2= safely places objects so as to minimize the hazard of falling objects, 1= safely places objects so as to minimize the hazard of falling objects with only verbal prompts	NEEDS CLOSE SUPERVISION
WS 16	0 1 2 0 1 2 0 1 2 0 1 2	Avoids danger related to electricity	Learner will avoid danger related to electricity.	Does learner avoid danger related to electricity?	Down power lines, frayed electrical cords, too many plugs in outlet, water and electrical outlets, etc.	2= describes 4 situations that are dangerous due to the presence of electricity and describes strategies to prevent or avoid those dangers, 1= safely plugs in and removes electrical cords	NEEDS CLOSE SUPERVISION

The AFLS® - Vocational Skills Protocol

The Assessment of Functional Living Skills - The AFLS®

Workplace Safety (Continued)

TASK	SCORE	TASK NAME	TASK OBJECTIVE	QUESTION	EXAMPLE	CRITERIA	COMMENT
WS 17	0 1 2 0 1 2 0 1 2 0 1 2	Avoids danger related to vehicles or moving equipment	Learner will monitor immediate area to avoid dangers from vehicles and moving equipment.	Does learner monitor immediate area for vehicles and moving equipment?	Motor vehicles, fork lifts, people using furniture dollies, etc.	2= monitors immediate area for moving equipment and vehicles and moves away from or safely avoids those dangers, 1= moves away from vehicles or moving equipment when warned by others	NEEDS CLOSE SUPERVISION
WS 18	0 1 2 0 1 2 0 1 2 0 1 2	Avoids dangers related to machinery	Learner will avoid dangers related to machinery.	Does learner avoid dangers related to machinery?	Machinery that may start up automatically, fans, machines with belts, motors, or other moving parts, etc.	2= identifies and avoids dangers associated with machinery, 1= avoids dangers associated with machinery after those dangers are identified by a supervisor	NEEDS CLOSE SUPERVISION
WS 19	0 1 2 0 1 2 0 1 2 0 1 2	Avoids dangers related to blood or other bodily fluids	Learner will avoid dangers related to blood and other bodily fluids.	Does learner avoid dangers related to blood and other bodily fluids?	Puts on latex gloves prior to cleaning up vomit on the floor, disposes into appropriate container, sanitizes area, etc.	2= avoids skin contact with blood and other bodily fluids, wears gloves prior to handling bodily fluids, disposes of fluids and cleaning materials by placing in an appropriate receptacle, reports to supervisor, 1= avoids skin contact with blood or other bodily fluids	NEEDS CLOSE SUPERVISION
WS 20	0 1 2 0 1 2 0 1 2 0 1 2	Avoids dangers related to harmful plants and animals	Learner will avoid dangers related to harmful plants and animals.	Does learner avoid dangers related to harmful plants and animals?	When working outside near bushes, is cautious to avoid poison ivy, snakes, spiders, etc.	2= identifies plants, animals, and insects that are dangerous and avoids those when necessary, 1= avoids dangerous plants, animals, and insects when told to do so	NEEDS CLOSE SUPERVISION

Use of safety equipment

TASK	SCORE	TASK NAME	TASK OBJECTIVE	QUESTION	EXAMPLE	CRITERIA	COMMENT
WS 21	0 1 2 0 1 2 0 1 2 0 1 2	Uses gloves	Learner will recognize conditions where gloves are necessary and put on gloves as needed to avoid injury to hands.	Does learner recognize conditions where gloves are necessary and put on gloves as needed to avoid injury to hands?	Latex gloves when cleaning up blood, rubber gloves when working with insecticides, and cloth or leather gloves to avoid scratches and cuts when handling rose bushes, etc.	2= identifies the type of gloves that are appropriate for different situations and puts on appropriate gloves prior to activity to protect self from injury, 1= wears gloves when needed with only verbal prompts	NEEDS CLOSE SUPERVISION
WS 22	0 1 2 0 1 2 0 1 2 0 1 2	Uses ear protection	Learner will demonstrate appropriate use of ear protection.	Does learner demonstrate appropriate use of ear protection?		2= wears ear protection in conditions that are loud or when intermittent loud noises are possible, 1= wears ear protection when needed with only verbal prompts	NEEDS CLOSE SUPERVISION

The AFLS® - Vocational Skills Protocol

The Assessment of Functional Living Skills - The AFLS®

Workplace Safety (Continued)

TASK	SCORE	TASK NAME	TASK OBJECTIVE	QUESTION	EXAMPLE	CRITERIA	COMMENT
WS 23	0 1 2 0 1 2 0 1 2 0 1 2	Uses eye protection	Learner will use eye protection in situations in which flying objects could injure eyes.	Does learner use eye protection in situations in which flying objects could injure eyes?	Leaf blower, lawn mower, trimmer, grinder, sander, etc.	2= wears eye protection in conditions that may contain flying debris, 1= wears eye protection when needed with only verbal prompts	NEEDS CLOSE SUPERVISION

Responding to emergencies

TASK	SCORE	TASK NAME	TASK OBJECTIVE	QUESTION	EXAMPLE	CRITERIA	COMMENT
WS 24	0 1 2 0 1 2 0 1 2 0 1 2	Responds appropriately to natural disasters	Learner will respond appropriately to natural disasters.	Can learner respond appropriately to natural disasters?	Fire, earthquake, tornado, flooding, etc.	2= describes appropriate actions to take during natural disaster (relevant for area in which learner is working), and takes those actions when required, 1= complies when told to take specific actions	
WS 25	0 1 2 0 1 2 0 1 2 0 1 2	Responds appropriately during medical emergencies	Learner will respond appropriately to medical emergencies.	Can learner respond appropriately to medical emergencies?	Heart attack, cut, choking on food item, slip and fall, shortness or breath, etc.	2= recognizes that a problem is occurring and seeks immediate help, 1= complies when told to take specific actions to assist in a medical emergency	NEEDS CLOSE SUPERVISION
WS 26	0 1 2 0 1 2 0 1 2 0 1 2	Responds appropriately to robbery or theft	Learner will respond appropriately to robbery or theft.	Can learner respond appropriately to robbery or theft?	Comply with demands of robber, remain calm, call authorities and notify supervisor immediately when safe to do so, etc.	2= describes what to do *if present* when robbery occurs, or discovers that theft has occurred, 1= describes what to do if discovers that theft has occurred	

Physical skills

TASK	SCORE	TASK NAME	TASK OBJECTIVE	QUESTION	EXAMPLE	CRITERIA	COMMENT
WS 27	0 1 2 3 4 0 1 2 3 4 0 1 2 3 4 0 1 2 3 4	Stands for long periods of time sufficient for most jobs	Learner will stand for long periods of time sufficient for most jobs.	Can learner stand for long periods of time sufficient for most jobs?		4= stands and performs tasks for 60 minutes, 3= stands and performs tasks for 45 minutes, 2= stands and performs tasks for 30 minutes, 1= stands and performs tasks for 10 minutes	Use of assistive device such as braces or a "stander" is acceptable when scoring as long as device or supports do not negatively impact job performance
WS 28	0 1 2 3 4 0 1 2 3 4 0 1 2 3 4 0 1 2 3 4	Walks for distances sufficient for most jobs	Learner will walk for distances sufficient for most jobs.	Can learner walk for distances sufficient for most jobs?		4= walks for 100 yards/meters, 3= walks for 50 yards/meters, 2= walks for 25 yards/meters, 1= walks for 10 yards/meters	

The AFLS® - Vocational Skills Protocol

The Assessment of Functional Living Skills - The AFLS®

Workplace Safety (Continued)

TASK	SCORE	TASK NAME	TASK OBJECTIVE	QUESTION	EXAMPLE	CRITERIA	COMMENT
WS 29	0 1 2 0 1 2 0 1 2 0 1 2	Propels wheelchair	Learner will self propel wheelchair appropriately for job requirements.	Does learner operate wheelchair effectively for position requirements?		2= propels, steers, and operates wheelchair appropriately for job requirements and job location, 1= propels, steers, and operates wheelchair appropriately only in larger open spaces or requires verbal or gestural prompts to operate appropriately in smaller or tighter settings (e.g., office cubicle area)	N/A for learners who do not use a wheel chair
WS 30	0 1 2 0 1 2 0 1 2 0 1 2	Performs variety of gross motor or whole-body tasks	Learner will demonstrate the coordination necessary to operate the equipment or materials required for the position.	Does learner demonstrate the coordination necessary to operate the equipment or materials required for the position?	Shoveling, watering garden, mowing lawn, etc.	2= demonstrates coordination with most tasks involving gross motor movements, 1= requires verbal or imitative prompts to perform new gross motor tasks	
WS 31	0 1 2 0 1 2 0 1 2 0 1 2	Performs variety of fine motor tasks	Learner will demonstrate the hand/eye coordination necessary to operate the equipment or materials required for the position.	Does learner demonstrate the hand/eye coordination necessary to operate the equipment or materials required for the position?	Pouring liquids into containers, sorting silverware, collating papers, making copies, align, stack	2= demonstrates hand/eye coordination with most tasks involving fine motor movements, 1= requires verbal or imitative prompts to perform new fine motor tasks	
WS 32	0 1 2 3 4 0 1 2 3 4 0 1 2 3 4 0 1 2 3 4	Correctly lifts items of various weights	Learner will correctly lift items of various weights.	Can learner correctly lift items of various weights?	Lifting with proper form to minimize injury to back is required for scoring such as bending at the knees and keeping back straight, etc.	4= assists others in lifting and carrying 100 lbs. for 10 feet, 3= lifts and carries 50 lbs. for 10 feet, 2= lifts and carries 25 lbs. for 10 feet, 1= lifts and carries 10 lbs. items for 10 ft.	NEEDS CLOSE SUPERVISION

The AFLS® - Vocational Skills Protocol

The Assessment of Functional Living Skills - The AFLS®

Workplace Safety (Continued)

TASK	SCORE	TASK NAME	TASK OBJECTIVE	QUESTION	EXAMPLE	CRITERIA	COMMENT
WS 33	0 1 2 0 1 2 0 1 2 0 1 2	Carries loose items and boxes	Learner will carry loose items and boxes.	Can learner carry loose items and boxes?	Carries a hammer, saw, small box, and an extension cord; carries box of paper, box of pencils, stapler, and post it notes, etc.	2= carries at least 4 items of a variety of shapes and sizes requiring the use of both hands for 30 yards/meters, 1= carries at least 2 items requiring only 1 hand for 30 yards/meters	
WS 34	0 1 2 0 1 2 0 1 2 0 1 2	Handles items with care	Learner will handle fragile, expensive, or important items with care.	Does learner handle fragile, expensive, or important items with care?		2= handles fragile, expensive, or important items in a safe manner, 1= requires occasional reminders to handle items in safe manner	
WS 35	0 1 2 0 1 2 0 1 2 0 1 2	Handles a variety of dangerous items	Learner will safely handle a variety of dangerous items.	Can learner safely handle a variety of dangerous items?	Poisonous, sharp, flammable, lethal, hot, dangerous, chemical, etc.	2= safely handles at least 4 different types of dangerous items or materials, 1= safely handles a very limited number of dangerous items or materials under direct supervision	NEEDS CLOSE SUPERVISION

The AFLS® - Vocational Skills Protocol

The Assessment of Functional Living Skills - The AFLS®

Fixed Activity Skills

Sort and count

TASK	SCORE	TASK NAME	TASK OBJECTIVE	QUESTION	EXAMPLE	CRITERIA	COMMENT
FA 1	0 1 2 0 1 2 0 1 2 0 1 2	Sorts items	Learner will sort items into groups.	Can learner sort items into groups?	Variables could include: size, color, type of shirt, etc. Categories could include clothing, books, hardware items, etc.	2= sorts items into at least 5 different categories using up to 5 different variables, 1= sorts into 2 categories by 2 variables	
FA 2	0 1 2 0 1 2 0 1 2 0 1 2	Uses counting tray	Learner will select designated number of items using a counting tray.	Can learner select designated number of items using a counting tray?	Places one screw into each section of an egg carton, dumps all 12 screws into small box	2= fills each section of a counting tray with a single part, transfers those pieces to a separate container, 1= fills each section of a counting tray with a single part with only verbal prompts	
FA 3	0 1 2 3 4 0 1 2 3 4 0 1 2 3 4 0 1 2 3 4	Counts and places items in bags	Learner will count and bag items.	Can learner count and bag items?	Counts out 12 screws, places in bag, and seals bag, once 50 bags are prepared, takes bags to a location to be boxed	4= counts and bags up to 50 mixed items and takes bags to specified location (if required), 3= counts and bags up to identical or mixed 30 items, 2= counts and bags up to 10 identical or mixed items, 1= requires verbal prompts to count and bag up to 10 identical items	

Packaging

TASK	SCORE	TASK NAME	TASK OBJECTIVE	QUESTION	EXAMPLE	CRITERIA	COMMENT
FA 4	0 1 2 0 1 2 0 1 2 0 1 2	Uses twist ties	Learner will fasten or hold things together using twist ties.	Can learner fasten or hold things together using twist ties?	Learner fastens display item to cardboard backing using twist tie, eals small plastic bag of nuts using twist tie, fastens a coil of wires together using twist tie, etc.	2= twists closure to ensure item is sealed or held together, 1= requires verbal prompts to twist items to seal or hold together	
FA 5	0 1 2 3 4 0 1 2 3 4 0 1 2 3 4 0 1 2 3 4	Shrink wraps	Learner will shrink wrap items.	Can learner shrink wrap items?		4= shrink wraps items both by operating a shrink wrapping machine and manually using sealing bags and a heat gun, 3= independently shrink wraps using sealing bags and a heat gun, requires only verbal prompts to shrink wrap using a shrink wrapping machine, 2= shrink wraps using sealing bags and a heat gun, 1= shrink wraps using sealing bags and a heat gun with only verbal prompts	

The AFLS® - Vocational Skills Protocol

The Assessment of Functional Living Skills - The AFLS®

Fixed Activity Skills (Continued)

Paper skills

TASK	SCORE	TASK NAME	TASK OBJECTIVE	QUESTION	EXAMPLE	CRITERIA	COMMENT
FA 6	0 1 2 0 1 2 0 1 2 0 1 2	Folds paper	Learner will fold paper into specified shape or size.	Can learner fold paper into a specified shape or size?	Neatly aligns edges of paper to fold in thirds to fit in an envelope	2= neatly aligns edges and folds paper into halves, quarters, or by specified shape or size, 1= folds papers in half	
FA 7	0 1 2 3 4 0 1 2 3 4 0 1 2 3 4 0 1 2 3 4	Shreds bulk papers	Learner will shred papers using a bulk shredder.	Can learner shred papers using a bulk shredder?		4= safely operates bulk shredding machine and changes "catch bin" as needed, 3= feeds paper into bulk shredder, turns on and off, and clears jams with only verbal prompts, 2= feeds paper into bulk shredder with minimal jamming, 1= feeds paper into a bulk shredder with only verbal prompts	NEEDS CLOSE SUPERVISION

Assembly skills

TASK	SCORE	TASK NAME	TASK OBJECTIVE	QUESTION	EXAMPLE	CRITERIA	COMMENT
FA 8	0 1 2 3 4 0 1 2 3 4 0 1 2 3 4 0 1 2 3 4	Assembles folders of information	Learner will assemble folders of information.	Can learner assemble folders of information?		4= collects designated number of pages from 5 or more stacks of papers, places neatly into folder in correct or designated order and on correct sides of folder, 3= collects designated number of pages from 2 stacks of papers and places neatly in folder on correct sides of folder, 2= places pack of pages given by someone else neatly into folder, 1= requires verbal prompts to place papers neatly into folder	
FA 9	0 1 2 0 1 2 0 1 2 0 1 2	Assembles items on assembly line	Learner will place items into a specified location as part of an assembly line assembly process.	Can learner place items into a specified location as part of an assembly line assembly process?		2= places single item in designated location with appropriate speed to maintain flow of assembly process, 1= places single item in designated location occasionally requiring to stop the flow of assembly process	

The AFLS® - Vocational Skills Protocol

The Assessment of Functional Living Skills - The AFLS®

Custodial and Cleaning
Specific cleaning issues

TASK	SCORE	TASK NAME	TASK OBJECTIVE	QUESTION	EXAMPLE	CRITERIA	COMMENT
CC 1	0 1 2 0 1 2 0 1 2 0 1 2	Cleans sinks	Learner will clean sinks.	Does learner clean sinks?		2= cleans sink bowl, faucets, and countertop area without leaving streaks or any scum, 1= cleans bowl, faucets, and counter with only verbal prompts	
CC 2	0 1 2 0 1 2 0 1 2 0 1 2	Cleans counter tops	Learner will clean counter tops.	Does learner clean counter tops?		2= cleans counter tops thoroughly without leaving residue, 1= wipes liquids from counter tops	
CC 3	0 1 2 0 1 2 0 1 2 0 1 2	Cleans windows and mirrors	Learner will clean windows and mirrors.	Does learner clean windows and mirrors?	Sprays cleaner on surface, wipes surface clean without leaving streaks	2= cleans windows and mirrors, 1= cleans windows and mirrors with only verbal prompts	
CC 4	0 1 2 0 1 2 0 1 2 0 1 2	Cleans walls	Learner will clean walls.	Does learner clean walls?	Uses cleaning spray, water, or cleaning wipes to clean food or other debris from walls	2= removes handprints, food, or other debris from walls, 1= removes food or other debris from walls with only verbal prompts	
CC 5	0 1 2 0 1 2 0 1 2 0 1 2	Cleans a toilet seat	Learner will use disinfectant spray and paper towel to clean a toilet seat.	Does learner adequately clean a toilet seat?	Sprays seat with a disinfectant and wipes clean with a paper towel	2= uses disinfectant spray and paper towel to clean a toilet seat and then washes hands, 1= requires only verbal prompts to spray toilet seat with disinfectant and wipe clean with a paper towel	NEEDS CLOSE SUPERVISION
CC 6	0 1 2 0 1 2 0 1 2 0 1 2	Cleans toilet using a toilet bowl brush	Learner will use a toilet brush and cleaning solution to clean toilet.	Does learner clean a toilet using a toilet brush?		2= uses toilet brush and cleaning solution to clean toilet, 1= uses toilet brush and cleaning solution to clean toilet with only verbal prompts	NEEDS CLOSE SUPERVISION
CC 7	0 1 2 3 4 0 1 2 3 4 0 1 2 3 4 0 1 2 3 4	Dusts objects	Learner will dust objects.	Does learner dust objects?		4= dusts any object, 3= dusts easy to reach objects but requires verbal assistance with objects overhead, blinds, etc., 2= moves objects to dust them and then returns objects to their usual location, 1= moves objects to dust them with only verbal prompts	

The AFLS® - Vocational Skills Protocol

The Assessment of Functional Living Skills - The AFLS®

Custodial and Cleaning (Continued)

TASK	SCORE	TASK NAME	TASK OBJECTIVE	QUESTION	EXAMPLE	CRITERIA	COMMENT
CC 8	0 1 2 0 1 2 0 1 2 0 1 2	Straightens objects	Learner will recognize when objects are out of alignment or cluttered and straighten so they are orderly.	Does learner straighten objects?		2= recognizes when objects are out of alignment or cluttered and straightens so they are orderly, 1= complies when told to straighten specific objects	
CC 9	0 1 2 0 1 2 0 1 2 0 1 2	Cleans a whiteboard	Learner will clean a whiteboard.	Does learner clean a whiteboard?		2= thoroughly cleans whiteboards, 1= cleans whiteboards with only verbal prompts	

Hotel housekeeping

TASK	SCORE	TASK NAME	TASK OBJECTIVE	QUESTION	EXAMPLE	CRITERIA	COMMENT
CC 10	0 1 2 0 1 2 0 1 2 0 1 2	Cleans bathtub	Learner will completely clean bathtub.	Does learner clean the bathtub?	Remove all soap scum, remove hair from drain, clean edges of tub, clean faucet, etc.	2= completely cleans bathtub, 1= cleans bathtub with only verbal prompts	
CC 11	0 1 2 0 1 2 0 1 2 0 1 2	Removes bedding	Learner will remove blankets, sheets, and pillow cases upon request.	Does learner remove bedding?		2= removes blankets, sheets and pillow cases, 1= removes blankets, sheets and pillow cases with only verbal prompts	
CC 12	0 1 2 0 1 2 0 1 2 0 1 2	Puts pillow into case	Learner will put pillow into case.	Does learner insert a pillow into a pillow case?		2= puts pillow into case, 1= puts pillow into case with imitative or minimal physical prompts	
CC 13	0 1 2 3 4 0 1 2 3 4 0 1 2 3 4 0 1 2 3 4	Puts sheets on bed	Learner will put clean sheets on a bed.	Does learner put sheets on a bed?		4= puts on both fitted sheet and a flat sheet, 3= independently puts on a flat sheet but requires verbal prompts to correctly put on a fitted sheet, 2= puts on either a flat or fitted sheet with only verbal prompts, 1= puts on either a flat or fitted sheet with minimal physical prompts	
CC 14	0 1 2 0 1 2 0 1 2 0 1 2	Makes bed	Learner will make a bed including sheets, pillow cases, blankets, and comforter or bedspread.	Does learner make bed?	Put on bottom sheet, then top sheet, then blankets, comforter, pillow cases, etc.	2= makes a bed including sheets, pillow cases, blankets, comforter or bedspread, 1= makes a bed with only verbal prompts	

The AFLS® - Vocational Skills Protocol

The Assessment of Functional Living Skills - The AFLS®

Custodial and Cleaning (Continued)

Cleaning floors

TASK	SCORE	TASK NAME	TASK OBJECTIVE	QUESTION	EXAMPLE	CRITERIA	COMMENT
CC 15	0 1 2 0 1 2 0 1 2 0 1 2	Sweeps and uses dustpan	Learner will sweep floor and use dustpan to pick up debris.	Does learner sweep floor and use dustpan to pick up debris?		2= sweeps floor debris into piles, sweeps piles into dustpan, and discards debris from dustpan into trash, 1= sweeps debris into piles	
CC 16	0 1 2 0 1 2 0 1 2 0 1 2	Vacuums floors	Learner will vacuum floors.	Does learner vacuum floors?		2= vacuums large areas without missing spots, vacuums around furniture or moves and replaces furniture as needed, vacuums stairs, dumps canister or discards full bag and replaces, 1= vacuums small areas without need to move or workaround furniture or other objects	
CC 17	0 1 2 0 1 2 0 1 2 0 1 2	Shampoos carpet	Learner will shampoo carpet.	Does learner shampoo carpet?		2= sets up carpet shampoo machine, adds cleaning fluids, shampoos carpets without missing areas, dumps dirty water, refills fluids, 1= shampoos carpet when machine is set up by someone else, requires someone else to change water and fluids	
CC 18	0 1 2 0 1 2 0 1 2 0 1 2	Spot cleans carpet	Learner will spot clean carpet.	Does learner spot clean carpet?		2= uses hand held spray or hot water to clean small spots on rug or carpet, 1= uses hand held spray or hot water to clean small spots on rug or carpet with only verbal prompts	
CC 19	0 1 2 3 4 0 1 2 3 4 0 1 2 3 4 0 1 2 3 4	Uses dust buster	Learner will use dust buster to vacuum small areas.	Does learner use dust buster to vacuum small areas?		4= vacuums small areas using handheld vacuum (Dust Buster) replaces filter and empties vacuum, 3= vacuums small areas using handheld vacuum replaces filter and empties vacuum with only verbal prompts, 2= vacuums small areas, 1= requires only verbal prompts to use handheld vacuum	
CC 20	0 1 2 0 1 2 0 1 2 0 1 2	Uses a Swiffer	Learner will Swiffer floors.	Does learner Swiffer floors?		2= applies new cleaning pad, swiffers section so it is free of debris, replaces cleaning pad when it no longer picks up debris (or when it is no longer wet), swiffers next section until entire area is clean, 1= swiffers small areas when someone else adds new pad to swiffer	

The AFLS® - Vocational Skills Protocol

Custodial and Cleaning (Continued)

TASK	SCORE	TASK NAME	TASK OBJECTIVE	QUESTION	EXAMPLE	CRITERIA	COMMENT
CC 21	0 1 2 3 4 0 1 2 3 4 0 1 2 3 4 0 1 2 3 4	Mops floor	Learner will mop floors.	Does learner mop floors?		4= gathers mop and bucket, adds hot water and cleaning liquids, mops area without leaving excess water behind, wrings out mop, changes water as needed, 3= gathers mop and bucket, adds hot water and cleaning liquids, mops area without leaving excess water behind, 2= mops area when water and cleaning solution is prepared for learner, 1= mops area with only verbal prompts	
CC 22	0 1 2 3 4 0 1 2 3 4 0 1 2 3 4 0 1 2 3 4	Strips, waxes, and buffs floor	Learner will strip, wax, and buff floors.	Does learner strip, wax, and buff floor?		4= uses floor stripper to remove existing wax on floor, adds new wax to floor, uses electric buffer to buff floors, 3= adds new wax to floor, uses electric buffer to buff floor, 2= operates electric buffer on floor, 1= operates electric buffer on floor with verbal prompts	

General cleaning issues

TASK	SCORE	TASK NAME	TASK OBJECTIVE	QUESTION	EXAMPLE	CRITERIA	COMMENT
CC 23	0 1 2 0 1 2 0 1 2 0 1 2	Recognizes when things need to be cleaned	Learner will determine what needs to be cleaned and straightened.	Does learner enter a room and determine what needs to be cleaned or straightened?	Recognizes that objects on floor need to be picked up and put away, the cement floor is dirty so a mop would be used to clean it, a small carpeted portion of the floor needs to be vacuumed, etc.	2= upon entering a room, determines what needs to be cleaned or straightened and identifies which cleaning tasks need to be done to make room clean and tidy, 1= upon entering a room, determines what needs to be cleaned or straightened	
CC 24	0 1 2 0 1 2 0 1 2 0 1 2	Rotates cleaning cloths	Learner will rotate cleaning cloths when cleaning.	Does learner rotate cleaning cloths when cleaning?		2= replaces cleaning clothes when dirty, 1= replaces cleaning cloths when directed to do so	
CC 25	0 1 2 0 1 2 0 1 2 0 1 2	Identifies appropriate chemicals or solutions for various cleaning tasks	Learner will identify appropriate chemicals or solutions for various cleaning tasks.	Can learner identify appropriate chemicals or solutions for various cleaning tasks?	Toilet cleaner, drain cleaner, countertop spray, wood floor cleaner, floor wax, window cleaner, etc.	2= receptively and expressively identifies cleaning products for use with at least 5 tasks, 1= receptively identifies correct cleaning products for 3 tasks	NEEDS CLOSE SUPERVISION
CC 26	0 1 2 0 1 2 0 1 2 0 1 2	Follows cleaning schedule	Learner will maintain a clean office or work area by following an established cleaning schedule.	Does learner consistently perform assigned cleaning tasks that have been agreed to based on a cleaning schedule?		2= maintains a clean office or work space by performing all cleaning task on a regular basis, 1= follows an established cleaning schedule when only provided with no more than one reminder per week	

The Assessment of Functional Living Skills - The AFLS®

Custodial and Cleaning (Continued)

Repair and resupply

TASK	SCORE	TASK NAME	TASK OBJECTIVE	QUESTION	EXAMPLE	CRITERIA	COMMENT
CC 27	0 1 2 0 1 2 0 1 2 0 1 2	Sorts recycling vs. trash	Learner will sort recycling/composting and trash.	Does learner discard trash and place recyclable/compostable items in a separate recycling/compost container?	Places plastic food wrappers in trash, newspaper into recycling, vegetable scraps into container for composting, etc.	2= places recycling (and/or composting items) in separate containers from trash, 1= sorts recycling (and/or composting items) from trash with only verbal prompts	
CC 28	0 1 2 0 1 2 0 1 2 0 1 2	Empties and disposes of trash	Learner will empty and dispose of trash.	Does learner empty and dispose of trash?		2= removes full bag from container or can, ties or seals bag, deposits into dumpster, 1= when given tied or sealed trash bag, deposits in dumpster	
CC 29	0 1 2 0 1 2 0 1 2 0 1 2	Replaces trash liners	Learner will replace trash liners.	Does learner replace trash liners?		2= places new trash bag into garbage can leaving edges of bag outside of can, 1= places new bag into can with only verbal prompts	
CC 30	0 1 2 0 1 2 0 1 2 0 1 2	Replaces toilet paper rolls	Learner will replace toilet paper rolls.	Does learner replace toilet paper roll when empty?		2= replaces toilet paper roll when needed, 1= locates a spare roll and changes toilet paper roll when asked to do so	
CC 31	0 1 2 0 1 2 0 1 2 0 1 2	Refills paper towel dispensers	Learner will refill paper towel dispensers.	Does learner refill paper towel dispensers?		2= refills paper towel dispensers when needed, 1= refills paper towel dispensers with only verbal prompts	
CC 32	0 1 2 0 1 2 0 1 2 0 1 2	Disposes of infectious or hazardous waste	Learner will dispose of infectious or hazardous waste.	Does learner dispose of infectious or hazardous waste?		2= follows recommended procedures and wears appropriate safety gear when handling and disposing or infectious or hazardous waste in a safe manner, 1= requires close supervision and verbal assistance to handle or dispose of infectious or hazardous waste	NEEDS CLOSE SUPERVISION

The AFLS® - Vocational Skills Protocol

The Assessment of Functional Living Skills - The AFLS®

Custodial and Cleaning (Continued)

TASK	SCORE	TASK NAME	TASK OBJECTIVE	QUESTION	EXAMPLE	CRITERIA	COMMENT
CC 33	0 1 2 3 4 0 1 2 3 4 0 1 2 3 4 0 1 2 3 4	Changes light bulbs	Learner will safely replace light bulbs and florescent tubes.	Does learner change light bulbs and florescent tubes?		4= turns off electricity and safely replaces both standard and fluorescent light bulbs as needed, including those that require the removal or opening of parts of fixtures on ceiling (glass covering), 3= turns off electricity and safely replaces both standard light bulbs and fluorescent tubes that can be reached while standing on the floor, 2= turns off electricity and safely replaces identical fluorescent tubes with only verbal prompts, 1= turns off electricity and safely replaces standard light bulbs with bulbs of identical wattage	NEEDS CLOSE SUPERVISION
CC 34	0 1 2 0 1 2 0 1 2 0 1 2	Uses correct light bulbs	Learner will state the importance of not using higher wattage light bulbs than specified for a fixture so as to avoid electrical fires.	Does learner know that using too high of a wattage light bulb can cause a fire?	Should not replace a 60 watt light bulb with a 120 watt light bulb when the light fixture specifies a maximum of a 60 watt bulb	2= safely turns off electricity to light before removing a light bulb and replaces it with a bulb with wattage equal to or less than the maximum specified for the light fixture, 1= safely turns off electricity to light before removing a light bulb and replacing bulb of equal wattage	NEEDS CLOSE SUPERVISION
CS 35	0 1 2 3 4 0 1 2 3 4 0 1 2 3 4 0 1 2 3 4	Stops running toilet	Learner will stop the water from running when needed.	Does learner stop running toilet?		4= manually closes stopper in tank, 3= seeks assistance when jiggling handle does not work to stop issue, 2= jiggles a toilet handle to stop the water from running when needed, 1= jiggles a toilet handle to stop the water from running with only verbal prompts	
CS 36	0 1 2 0 1 2 0 1 2 0 1 2	Clears and cleans drains	Learner will clear and clean drains.	Does learner clear and clean drains?	Using store-bought drain cleaner or by fishing clog out of drain with fingers or object	2= clears clogged or slow drains, 1= clears clogged or slow drains with only verbal prompts	SUPERVISION required if drain contains disposal or is otherwise dangerous

The AFLS® - Vocational Skills Protocol

The Assessment of Functional Living Skills - The AFLS®

Custodial and Cleaning (Continued)

Building environment and meetings

TASK	SCORE	TASK NAME	TASK OBJECTIVE	QUESTION	EXAMPLE	CRITERIA	COMMENT
CS 37	0 1 2 3 4 0 1 2 3 4 0 1 2 3 4 0 1 2 3 4	Sets up rooms for meetings	Learner will set up rooms for meetings.	Does learner set up rooms for meetings?		4= when told how many people will be in attendance for meeting, ensures tables and chairs are set up to accommodate audience, sets out drinks, pens, paper, etc., as required for meeting, 3= follows written list to ensures tables and chairs are set up to accommodate audience numbers, sets out drinks, pens, paper, etc., as required for meeting, 2= assemble and set up table and chairs in rows or other arrangements as needed for meeting, 1= places chairs next to tables with only verbal prompts when tables have been arranged by someone else	
CS 38	0 1 2 0 1 2 0 1 2 0 1 2	Breaks down rooms after events	Learner will break down rooms after events.	Does learner break down rooms after events?		2= folds or moves tables to designated location, folds, stacks, or moves chairs, cleans up unused materials, 1= folds chairs or tables when breaking down room with another person	
CS 39	0 1 2 0 1 2 0 1 2 0 1 2	Adjusts air conditioning and heat	Learner will adjust air conditioning and heat.	Does learner adjust air-conditioning and heat?	Adjust room temperature by changing the thermostat setting to "Heat" prior to adjusting temperature to 72 degrees	2= adjusts thermostat using appropriate and reasonable temperature change when told room is too hot or too cold, adjusts window or portable AC or heaters, 1= adjusts thermostat to exact temperature when told	
CS 40	0 1 2 0 1 2 0 1 2 0 1 2	Locks and unlocks doors	Learner will lock and unlock doors.	Can learner lock and unlock doors?	Padlocks, combination locks, push-button keypads, twist locks, deadbolts, etc.	2= locks and unlocks all types of door, cabinet, and padlocks including combination locks, 1= uses keys to locks and unlocks all types of door and cabinet locks	
CS 41	0 1 2 3 4 0 1 2 3 4 0 1 2 3 4 0 1 2 3 4	Operates security system	Learner will set and cancel alarm system.	Does learner follow the procedures to set and turn of a security alarm system?		4= consistently sets and deactivates security system, and knows how to contact alarm company when accidentally activated, 3= consistently sets and deactivates security system, 2= consistently deactivates security system, 1= activates and deactivates security system with only verbal prompts	

The AFLS® - Vocational Skills Protocol

The Assessment of Functional Living Skills - The AFLS®

Custodial and Cleaning (Continued)

Safety and security issues

TASK	SCORE	TASK NAME	TASK OBJECTIVE	QUESTION	EXAMPLE	CRITERIA	COMMENT
CS 42	0 1 2 3 4 0 1 2 3 4 0 1 2 3 4 0 1 2 3 4	Works safely around sensitive equipment and items	Learner will work safely around sensitive equipment and items.	Does learner work safely around sensitive equipment and items?	Fragile, expensive, private items, computers, AV equipment, etc.	4= handles and cleans around sensitive or fragile equipment or objects without breaking, damaging, or misplacing, 3= handles and cleans around sensitive or fragile equipment or objects with verbal prompts, 2= cleans around sensitive materials and fragile items under close supervision often requiring supervisor to handle those items while areas are being cleaned, 1= identifies items that are sensitive or fragile	
CS 43	0 1 2 0 1 2 0 1 2 0 1 2	Respects others personal possessions and private items while working	Learner will not touch personal possessions or organized work materials of others while working.	Does learner work without touching personal possessions or organized work material of others?		2= avoids touching others' belongings, looking into personal possessions such as purses and desk drawers, 1= states items that are personal or private and should not be touched while cleaning	
CS 44	0 1 2 0 1 2 0 1 2 0 1 2	Identifies and reports problems needing immediate repair	Learner will identify and report problems needing immediate repair.	Does learner identify and report problems needing immediate repair?	Informs supervisor/ owner that there is a leak under the sink that requires a plumber to fix	2= identifies situations that if not immediately addressed could cause or lead to further damage or a worsening situation, notifies supervisor or owner of situation emphasizing the immediate need for attention, 1= reports issues to supervisor but does not stress importance or immediacy of the need to address the issue	
CS 45	0 1 2 0 1 2 0 1 2 0 1 2	Identifies and reports problems that require specialized help or services	Learner will identify and report problems that require specialized help or services.	Can learner identify and report problems that require specialized help or services?	Leaky roof, broken lock, electrical, plumbing, computer failure, broken window, etc.	2= identifies at least 5 different professionals to contact in order to address specific problems, 1= states who to contact for electrical and plumbing issues	
CS 46	0 1 2 0 1 2 0 1 2 0 1 2	Uses caution signs or cones	Learner will identify when to use caution signs or cones.	Can learner identify when to use caution signs or cones?	Places "Wet Floor" sign in area to be mopped	2= states at least 3 situations that would require the use of cones or caution signs and sets up cones or signs, 1= states 1 situation that would require the use of cones or signs and sets up cones where directed by supervisor	
CS 47	0 1 2 0 1 2 0 1 2 0 1 2	Keeps doors locked after cleaning	Learner will keep doors locked after cleaning.	Does learner keep doors locked after cleaning?		2= consistently relocks doors after cleaning rooms, 1= needs occasional reminders to relock doors after cleaning rooms	

The AFLS® - Vocational Skills Protocol

The Assessment of Functional Living Skills - The AFLS®

Laundry

TASK	SCORE	TASK NAME	TASK OBJECTIVE	QUESTION	EXAMPLE	CRITERIA	COMMENT
LY 1	0 1 2 0 1 2 0 1 2 0 1 2	Sorts laundry by color	Learner will sort colored and white clothing for washing.	Does learner sort laundry into appropriate piles for whites and colors?	Learner puts all whites into one pile and dark colors into another pile	2= sorts colors and white clothing for washing, 1= sorts colors and white clothing for washing with only verbal prompts	
LY 2	0 1 2 3 4 0 1 2 3 4 0 1 2 3 4 0 1 2 3 4	Uses washing machine	Learner will operate washing machine to wash clothes.	Does learner wash clothes in washing machine?	Measure and add soap, add clothes, adjust settings, turn on washer, and remove clothes from washer	4= independently puts correct amount of clothes in washer, adds soap, and selects appropriate settings, 3= puts clothes in washer when given by caregiver, adds soap, and selects appropriate settings, 2= puts clothes in washer, adds correct amount of soap, and turns on washer but requires verbal prompts to select the appropriate settings, 1= puts clothes in washer and adds measured soap with only verbal prompts	
LY 3	0 1 2 0 1 2 0 1 2 0 1 2	Puts clothes in dryer	Learner will move items from washer to dryer.	Does learner put clothes in dryer?		2= moves items from washer to dryer, 1= moves items from washer to dryer with only verbal prompts	
LY 4	0 1 2 3 4 0 1 2 3 4 0 1 2 3 4 0 1 2 3 4	Uses dryer	Learner will put clothes in dryer, add dryer sheet, clean lint trap, and follow directions to push buttons/turn dial for correct settings.	Does learner dry clothes in dryer?		4= puts clothes in dryer, adds dryer sheet, cleans lint trap, follows directions to push buttons/turn dial for correct settings, and turns on dryer, 3= puts clothes in dryer, adds dryer sheet, cleans lint trap, and turns on dryer, but does not select settings, 2= puts clothes in dryer, adds dryer sheet, and cleans lint trap, 1= puts clothes in dryer with only verbal prompts	
LY 5	0 1 2 0 1 2 0 1 2 0 1 2	Empties dryer	Learner will empty all items from dryer into a laundry basket.	Does learner remove clothes from dryer?		2= empties all items from dryer into a laundry basket, 1= empties items into a laundry basket with only verbal prompts	
LY 6	0 1 2 0 1 2 0 1 2 0 1 2	Brings clothes to an area to be folded	Learner will bring clothes to an area to be folded.	Does learner bring clothes to an area to be folded?		2= brings basket of recently cleaned clothes to an area to be folded, 1= brings basket of recently cleaned clothes to an area to be folded with only verbal prompts	

The AFLS® - Vocational Skills Protocol

The Assessment of Functional Living Skills - The AFLS®

Laundry (Continued)

TASK	SCORE	TASK NAME	TASK OBJECTIVE	QUESTION	EXAMPLE	CRITERIA	COMMENT
LY 7	0 1 2 0 1 2 0 1 2 0 1 2	Separates laundry items prior to folding	Learner will separate laundry items into similar articles.	Can learner separate the laundry items into similar articles?	Sort shirts, pants, socks, towels, etc. into different piles	2= separates laundry items into piles of similar articles, 1= requires only imitative or verbal prompts to separate different types of laundry articles	
LY 8	0 1 2 0 1 2 0 1 2 0 1 2	Folds towels	Learner will fold, stack, and put away towels.	Does learner fold and put away towels?		2= folds towels, 1= folds a towel only with verbal prompts	
LY 9	0 1 2 0 1 2 0 1 2 0 1 2	Matches and connects socks	Learner will match and connect all sock pairs.	Does learner match and connect socks when given an assortment of different socks?	Learner finds two socks with same stripes and connects them	2= matches and connects all sock pairs, 1= matches and connects sock pairs with only verbal prompts	
LY 10	0 1 2 0 1 2 0 1 2 0 1 2	Folds pants	Learner will fold pants neatly and stack in piles or place on hangers.	Does learner fold pants?		2= folds all pants, stacks neatly into a pile, or places on hangers, 1= folds pants with only verbal prompts	
LY 11	0 1 2 0 1 2 0 1 2 0 1 2	Folds and puts away undershirts	Learner will fold and stack undershirts.	Does learner fold and stack undershirts?		2= folds and stacks all undershirts 1= folds and stacks all undershirts when provided with only verbal prompts	
LY 12	0 1 2 0 1 2 0 1 2 0 1 2	Folds and stacks shirts	Learner will fold shirts.	Does learner fold shirts?		2= folds all (non-hanging) shirt types and stacks neatly into a pile, 1= folds all (non-hanging) shirts with only verbal prompts	
LY 13	0 1 2 0 1 2 0 1 2 0 1 2	Folds and stacks sheets	Learner will fold sheets.	Does learner fold sheets?		2= folds and stacks sheets, 1= requires verbal prompts to fold a sheet	
LY 14	0 1 2 0 1 2 0 1 2 0 1 2	Identifies damaged clothing	Learner will identify clothing that is stained, worn-out, or needs to be repaired.	Does learner know when clothing items need to be discarded or repaired?	Shirt requires a button, socks with holes and shirts with tears or stains to be discarded, shoes with significant wear or holes to be replaced, etc.	2= identifies laundry items that need to be discarded or repaired, 1= requires only verbal prompts to identify laundry items that need to be discarded or replaced	

The AFLS® - Vocational Skills Protocol

The Assessment of Functional Living Skills - The AFLS®

Retail

Product and box issues

TASK	SCORE	TASK NAME	TASK OBJECTIVE	QUESTION	EXAMPLE	CRITERIA	COMMENT
RT 1	0 1 2 / 0 1 2 / 0 1 2 / 0 1 2	Receptively identifies products	Learner will receptively identify products.	Can learner receptively identify products?		2= receptively identifies at least 25 products, 1= receptively identifies 10 products	
RT 2	0 1 2 / 0 1 2 / 0 1 2 / 0 1 2	Labels products	Learner will label products.	Can learner label products?		2= labels at least 25 products, 1= labels 10 products	
RT 3	0 1 2 3 4 / 0 1 2 3 4 / 0 1 2 3 4 / 0 1 2 3 4	Loads boxes into storage area	Learner will load boxes into storage area.	Can learner load boxes into storage area?		4= stacks boxes (up to 50 lbs.) onto hand truck and uses hand truck to move stacks, places individual boxes into correct location, 3= stacks boxes (up to 30 lbs.) onto hand truck and uses hand truck to move stacks, places individual boxes into correct location, 2= stacks boxes (up to 20 lbs.) onto hand truck and uses hand truck to move stacks, places individual boxes into correct location, 1= carries individual boxes up to 15 lbs. and places in correct location	NEEDS CLOSE SUPERVISION
RT 4	0 1 2 / 0 1 2 / 0 1 2 / 0 1 2	Stacks boxes	Learner will stack boxes.	Can learner stack boxes?		2= stacks boxes (up to 50 lbs.) up to the height of learner's head so boxes are stable and aligned, 1= stacks boxes (up to 25 lbs.) 3 high	NEEDS CLOSE SUPERVISION
RT 5	0 1 2 / 0 1 2 / 0 1 2 / 0 1 2	Sorts boxed merchandise	Learner will sort boxed merchandise.	Can learner sort boxed merchandise?	When a box is received containing multiple items inside, sorts items by reading the labels, color, size, area of store, etc.	2= sorts merchandise based on 4 different variables, 1= sorts merchandise based on 2 different variables	

Pricing skills

TASK	SCORE	TASK NAME	TASK OBJECTIVE	QUESTION	EXAMPLE	CRITERIA	COMMENT
RT 6	0 1 2 / 0 1 2 / 0 1 2 / 0 1 2	Attaches price tags	Learner will attach price tags.	Can learner attach price tags?	Shoots plastic tag fastener into garments, uses sticker gun to roll price stickers onto cans of food, etc.	2= uses price tag labeler (gun) to attach tags to items, 1= attaches sticker prices to items	NEEDS CLOSE SUPERVISION
RT 7	0 1 2 / 0 1 2 / 0 1 2 / 0 1 2	Sets up price tag labeling machines	Learner will set up price tag labeling machines.	Can learner set up price tag labeling machines?		2= creates labels or tags using tag machine, 1= creates tags with only verbal prompts	

The AFLS® - Vocational Skills Protocol

The Assessment of Functional Living Skills - The AFLS®

Retail (continued)

TASK	SCORE	TASK NAME	TASK OBJECTIVE	QUESTION	EXAMPLE	CRITERIA	COMMENT
RT 8	0 1 2 0 1 2 0 1 2 0 1 2	Stocks shelves with cans, bottles, boxes, etc.	Learner will stocks shelves with cans, bottles, boxes, etc.	Can learner stocks shelves with cans, bottles, boxes, etc.?	Label of item facing forward, in a straight row, evenly spaced, etc.	2= stocks shelves with cans, boxes, bottles, etc. so that items are neatly aligned, 1= stocks shelves but requires verbal prompts to ensure items are neat and aligned	

Clothing related

TASK	SCORE	TASK NAME	TASK OBJECTIVE	QUESTION	EXAMPLE	CRITERIA	COMMENT
RT 9	0 1 2 0 1 2 0 1 2 0 1 2	Discriminates sizes of garments	Learner will discriminate garment sizes.	Can learner discriminate garment sizes?		2= receptively and expressively identifies garments of different sizes, sorts by size, 1= receptively identifies garment sizes	
RT 10	0 1 2 0 1 2 0 1 2 0 1 2	Hangs clothing	Learner will hang clothing.	Can learner hang clothing?		2= hangs garments on hangers and places hangers neatly onto racks by size, 1= places garments already on hangers onto racks	
RT 11	0 1 2 0 1 2 0 1 2 0 1 2	Folds and stacks clothing items	Learner will fold and stack clothing.	Can learner fold clothing?	Folds t-shirts to specified size and places neatly back onto display shelf	2= folds any clothing item in accordance with store standard and places onto existing stacks, 1= folds 1 type of clothing in accordance with store standards	
RT 12	0 1 2 0 1 2 0 1 2 0 1 2	Arranges clothing items on displays	Learner will arrange clothing items on displays.	Can learner arrange clothing items on displays?		2= arranges clothing neatly into stacks on store displays by size or color, 1= arranges clothing neatly into stacks on store displays by size or color with verbal prompts	
RT 13	0 1 2 0 1 2 0 1 2 0 1 2	Dresses mannequin	Learner will dress a mannequin.	Can learner dress a mannequin?	Learner places newly arrived merchandise on mannequin in accordance with picture model sent from the corporate headquarters	2= dresses a mannequin, 1= dresses a mannequin with verbal prompts	

Maintaining store

TASK	SCORE	TASK NAME	TASK OBJECTIVE	QUESTION	EXAMPLE	CRITERIA	COMMENT
RT 14	0 1 2 0 1 2 0 1 2 0 1 2	Gathers shopping carts	Learner will gather shopping carts.	Can learner gather shopping carts?	Safely scans parking lot for shopping carts, gathers carts in parking lot and from cart returns, stacks carts and pushes carts (using power assisted device if available at store) back to store, stacks retrieved carts back in location for customers	2= brings shopping carts back to store from designated shopping cart return areas, 1= gathers lone carts in parking lot and brings to designated shopping cart return areas	NEEDS CLOSE SUPERVISION

The AFLS® - Vocational Skills Protocol

The Assessment of Functional Living Skills - The AFLS®

Retail (continued)

TASK	SCORE	TASK NAME	TASK OBJECTIVE	QUESTION	EXAMPLE	CRITERIA	COMMENT
RT 15	0 1 2 0 1 2 0 1 2 0 1 2	Sets up displays	Learner will set up displays.	Can learner set up displays?		2= assembles displays of various products, 1= assembles displays of various products with only verbal prompts	
RT 16	0 1 2 3 4 0 1 2 3 4 0 1 2 3 4 0 1 2 3 4	Assembles items with various parts	Learner will follow written or picture diagram directions to assemble items with multiple parts.	Can learner follow written or picture diagram directions to assemble items with multiple parts?	Places a lamp shade on a lamp and screws it to base, Follows directions to assemble a child's bike to be used in a toy store display	4= follows written or picture diagrams to assemble at least 20 parts, 3= follows written or picture diagrams to assemble at least 10 parts, 2= assembles 5 parts, 1= requires step-by-step verbal directions to assemble 2 parts	

Interactions with customers

TASK	SCORE	TASK NAME	TASK OBJECTIVE	QUESTION	EXAMPLE	CRITERIA	COMMENT
RT 17	0 1 2 0 1 2 0 1 2 0 1 2	Greets and assists customers	Learner will greet and assist customers.	Can learner greet and assist customers?	Where's the restroom? Does this come in a large? Can you tell me where the light bulbs are? etc.	2= answers customers questions about products and store locations, politely tells customer to wait while supervisor or coworker is contacted to find answers when answer is unknown, 1= greets customers	
RT 18	0 1 2 0 1 2 0 1 2 0 1 2	Interacts appropriately with customers	Learner will interact appropriately with customers.	Does learner interact appropriately with customers?		2= consistently uses polite language and good manners when interacting with customers, 1= requires verbal prompts to interact with customers appropriately	
RT 19	0 1 2 0 1 2 0 1 2 0 1 2	Sells products	Learner will sell products.	Can learner sell products?		2= knowledgeable about products, answers customers questions, provides information about products relative to other comparable products, describes benefits of products, 1= knowledgeable about products and answers customers questions related to product line	
RT 20	0 1 2 0 1 2 0 1 2 0 1 2	Checks storeroom for specific merchandise	Learner will check storeroom for specific merchandise.	Can learner check storeroom for specific merchandise?		2= upon customer request or when availability is unknown based on items on display learner checks storeroom for requested item or specific size or item variation, 1= checks storeroom for specific item when asked by supervisor	

The AFLS® - Vocational Skills Protocol

The Assessment of Functional Living Skills - The AFLS®

Retail (continued)

TASK	SCORE	TASK NAME	TASK OBJECTIVE	QUESTION	EXAMPLE	CRITERIA	COMMENT
RT 21	0 1 2 3 4 0 1 2 3 4 0 1 2 3 4 0 1 2 3 4	Uses cash register	Learner will check out customers at cash register.	Can learner check out customers using a cash register?		4= scans products by UPC or bar code, requests pricing information from supervisor for unmarked items, weighs produce, enters pricing information into register "by hand," moves items to bagging area, states total to customer, asks for store loyalty or discount card, applies coupons, accepts debit card payments, accepts cash, dispenses correct change, 3= scans products by UPC or bar code, weighs produce, moves items to bagging area, states total to customer, asks for store loyalty or discount card, applies coupons, accepts debit card payments, 2= scans products by UPC or bar code, moves items to bagging area, states total to customer, accepts debit card payments, 1= scans products by UPC or bar code, moves items to bagging area	
RT 22	0 1 2 0 1 2 0 1 2 0 1 2	Bags items	Learner will bags items.	Can learner bag items?		2= places items in bags without over or under filling bags, places lighter or fragile items on top of heavier items, individually wraps or double bags specialty items, 1= places items in bag with only verbal prompts	

The AFLS® - Vocational Skills Protocol

The Assessment of Functional Living Skills - The AFLS®

Support Personnel

TASK	SCORE	TASK NAME	TASK OBJECTIVE	QUESTION	EXAMPLE	CRITERIA	COMMENT
SP 1	0 1 2 0 1 2 0 1 2 0 1 2	Cleans up toys and equipment	Learner will clean up and put away toys or recreational equipment from play or recreation areas.	Can learner clean up and put away toys and recreational equipment?	In child care center, places all toys back on shelves, places buckets of Legos back in closet, picks up and trash on floor, etc. In a geriatric center, returns books and magazines to proper shelves, places board games back in box, wraps rubber bands around playing cards, etc.	2= cleans play or recreational area by putting toys and recreational equipment where those items are typically stored, straightens area, and rearranges any furniture, 1= cleans play or recreational area by putting toys and recreational equipment where those items are typically stored with only verbal prompts	
SP 2	0 1 2 0 1 2 0 1 2 0 1 2	Reads books to a group	Learner will read books to small groups .	Can learner read books to small groups?		2= sits and holds book in such a way that any pictures in book can be viewed by the group, reads clearly and loudly enough to be heard by group, 1= reads books to group but requires verbal prompts or reminders to hold book or position self in a way that allows group to view pictures	
SP 3	0 1 2 0 1 2 0 1 2 0 1 2	Serves snack foods and drinks	Learner will serve snack foods and drinks.	Can learner carry, set up, and distribute snack foods and drinks?	Carries bottle of juice to table, arranges cups to accommodate each child, pours juice into each cup without spilling, places small plates out in front of each chair, places a small pile of goldfish on each plate, etc.	2= carries, place sets, pours drinks without spilling, places even amounts of food and snacks on individual plates for groups, 1= sets table so each person has a cup, flatware, and a plate	
SP 4	0 1 2 0 1 2 0 1 2 0 1 2	Performs a variety of classroom or center-based tasks	Learner will follow directions to perform a variety of tasks designed to assist and center-based tasks designed to assist a lead teacher or group leader.	Does learner perform a variety of tasks designed to assist the teacher or group leader?	For geriatric center: roll individuals in wheelchairs from day room to bedrooms, retrieves materials on demand, etc. For day care: runs attendance documents to front office, takes role, passes out musical instruments, turns on DVD player, etc.	2= performs all tasks given by teacher or group leader with positive attitude, 1= performs tasks in room or in limited space but not those that require independent movement around the building	

The AFLS® - Vocational Skills Protocol

The Assessment of Functional Living Skills - The AFLS®

Support Personnel (Continued)

TASK	SCORE	TASK NAME	TASK OBJECTIVE	QUESTION	EXAMPLE	CRITERIA	COMMENT
SP 5	0 1 2 0 1 2 0 1 2 0 1 2	Plays games	Learner will play a variety of games with the students (or residents).	Can learner play games with the students/residents?	For day care: duck duck goose, red light green light, tag, etc. For geriatric center: gin rummy, go fish, hokey pokey, checkers, etc.	2= plays and leads at least 5 games appropriate and approved for the setting, 1= plays and leads at least 2 games appropriate and approved for the setting	
SP 6	0 1 2 0 1 2 0 1 2 0 1 2	Monitors recreational space (playground or day room)	Learner will monitor recreational space (play ground or day room).	Does learner monitor recreational space?	Monitors space to ensure rules are being followed, safe activities are being played, etc.	2= states the range of acceptable activities given the space, monitors the space for rule following and generally appropriate behavior, reports instances of rule violations to supervisors, helps kids or residents with simple tasks such as typing their shoes, setting up recreational equipment, etc., 1= states the range of acceptable activities given the space	

The AFLS® - Vocational Skills Protocol

Office Skills

Office machines and tools

TASK	SCORE	TASK NAME	TASK OBJECTIVE	QUESTION	EXAMPLE	CRITERIA	COMMENT
OF 1	0 1 2 3 4 0 1 2 3 4 0 1 2 3 4 0 1 2 3 4	Makes copies	Learner will make copies.	Can learner make copies?	Basic functions include cancel print job, black and white or color, 1 or 2 sided, collated or separated by page, stapled, enlarged, landscape or portrait, dark-light contrast settings, etc.	4= operates copier using all basic functions, 3= makes multiple copies of single sheets by entering desired number into keypad, 2= places pages to be copied in feeder tray **and** aligns pages on glass, pushes button to copy without changing any settings, 1= places single sheet into feeder tray **or** on glass and makes single copy	
OF 2	0 1 2 3 4 0 1 2 3 4 0 1 2 3 4 0 1 2 3 4	Maintains photocopier	Learner will resolve minor issues with photocopier.	Can learner resolve minor issues with photocopier?		4= replenishes paper and ink/toner, attempts to clear more complex paper jams, notifies supervisor when unable to fix the jam, 3= replaces ink or toner cartridges when needed, 2= clears paper jams that only require opening a compartment door to remove paper, 1= replenishes paper when needed	
OF 3	0 1 2 3 4 0 1 2 3 4 0 1 2 3 4 0 1 2 3 4	Collates papers	Learner will collate papers.	Can learner collate papers?	Learner takes page 1 and places it on page 2, then takes pages 1 and 2 and places them on page 3, all 3 pages are then placed as a group next to the single pages, the next group is turned 90 degrees and placed on the previous collated stack to keep them separated and organized, etc.	4= collates papers from up to 10 different stacks of paper each containing at least 10 pages, 3= collates from 3 different piles, up to 5 times, keeping collated groups organized, 2= collates papers from 3 different stacks of paper each containing 1 page each, 1= collates papers from 3 different stacks of paper each containing 1 page each with only verbal prompts	
OF 4	0 1 2 3 4 0 1 2 3 4 0 1 2 3 4 0 1 2 3 4	Staples papers	Learner will staple papers.	Can learner staple papers?		4= selects appropriate stapler based on number of pages to be stapled, staples up to 50 pages, replenishes staples when needed, and clears jammed staples, 3= selects appropriate stapler based on number of pages to be stapled, staples up to 50 pages, and replenishes staples when needed, 2= replenishes staples when needed, 1= neatly arranges papers and staples up to 10 pages of the same size paper	

The AFLS® - Vocational Skills Protocol

The Assessment of Functional Living Skills - The AFLS®

Office Skills (Continued)

TASK	SCORE	TASK NAME	TASK OBJECTIVE	QUESTION	EXAMPLE	CRITERIA	COMMENT
OF 5	0 1 2 0 1 2 0 1 2 0 1 2	Removes staples	Learner will remove staples.	Can learner remove staples?		2= removes staples without damaging papers, 1= removes staples with only verbal prompts	
OF 6	0 1 2 3 4 0 1 2 3 4 0 1 2 3 4 0 1 2 3 4	Uses a 3-hole punch	Learner will use a 3-hole punch.	Can learner use a 3-hole punch?	Places sheets of paper into a 3-hole punch so that papers are aligned top and bottom and side to side	4= punches holes after adjusting alignment settings and empties punched holes without spilling onto floor, 3= from larger stack of papers, places and aligns smaller number of papers into 3-hole punch so that the hole of larger stack align in a uniform manner, 2= aligns and places at least 5 sheets of paper into 3 hole punch and punches holes, 1= aligns and places at least 5 sheets of paper into 3 hole punch and punches holes with only verbal prompts	
OF 7	0 1 2 3 4 0 1 2 3 4 0 1 2 3 4 0 1 2 3 4	Uses a 3-ring binder	Learner will set up and label binder dividers.	Does learner organize 3-ring binders?	Neatly writes the days of the week on binder divider tabs to organize employee work schedules, etc.	4= sets up and labels binder dividers to organize content into sections, 3= sets up and organizes materials in a binder using dividers with verbal prompts, 2= opens and closes a 3-ring binder to insert and remove papers, 1= opens and closes a 3-ring binder to insert or remove papers with only verbal prompts	
OF 8	0 1 2 0 1 2 0 1 2 0 1 2	Uses paperclips and other fasteners	Learner will select and use appropriate paperclips and other fasteners.	Can learner select and use appropriate paperclips and other fasteners?	Rubber bands, alligator clips, paperclips of different sizes, etc.	2= selects and uses appropriate size and type of fastener, 1= places paperclips to fasten 10 pages	
OF 9	0 1 2 0 1 2 0 1 2 0 1 2	Uses pushpins or thumb tacks	Learner will use pushpins or thumb tacks.	Can learner use pushpins or thumb tacks?		2= attaches papers to wall with pushpins or tacks, 1= requires verbal prompts to attach papers to wall with pushpins or tacks	
OF 10	0 1 2 0 1 2 0 1 2 0 1 2	Hangs papers using magnets	Learner will hang papers using magnets.	Can learner hang papers using magnets?		2= hangs papers to metal surfaces with magnets, 1= requires only verbal prompts to hang papers to metallic surfaces with magnets	

The Assessment of Functional Living Skills - The AFLS®

Office Skills (Continued)

TASK	SCORE	TASK NAME	TASK OBJECTIVE	QUESTION	EXAMPLE	CRITERIA	COMMENT
OF 11	0 1 2 3 4 0 1 2 3 4 0 1 2 3 4 0 1 2 3 4	Uses pencil sharpeners	Learner will use a mechanical and an electric pencil sharpener.	Does learner use pencil sharpeners?		4= uses mechanical and electric pencil sharpeners, 3= uses electric sharpener but requires verbal prompts to sharpen pencil with mechanical sharpener, 2= uses an electric sharpener but requires some physical prompts to sharpen with a mechanical sharpener, 1= requires only verbal prompts to sharpen pencil with electric sharpener	
OF 12	0 1 2 0 1 2 0 1 2 0 1 2	Empties pencil sharpener	Learner will empty pencil sharpener.	Can learner empty pencil sharpener?		2= empties pencil sharpener without spilling shavings, 1= empties sharpener with only verbal prompts	
OF 13	0 1 2 0 1 2 0 1 2 0 1 2	Shreds papers	Learner will shred papers.	Can learner shred papers?		2= shreds papers, reverses or clears jams as needed, 1= shreds papers with only verbal prompts	NEEDS CLOSE SUPERVISION
OF 14	0 1 2 0 1 2 0 1 2 0 1 2	Empties shredder	Learner will empty shredder.	Can learner empty shredder?		2= empties shredder without spilling shredded papers 1= empties shredder with only verbal prompts	NEEDS CLOSE SUPERVISION
OF 15	0 1 2 3 4 0 1 2 3 4 0 1 2 3 4 0 1 2 3 4	Uses a paper cutter	Learner will use paper cutter to cut paper.	Can learner use a paper cutter to cut papers?		4= safely aligns, measures, and cuts at least 3 sheets of paper at once, to a specified dimension, 3= safely aligns, measures, and cuts a single sheet of paper to a specified dimension, 2= safely aligns and cuts single sheet in half, 1= cuts papers in half with only verbal prompts	NEEDS CLOSE SUPERVISION
OF 16	0 1 2 3 4 0 1 2 3 4 0 1 2 3 4 0 1 2 3 4	Uses a lamination machine	Learner will use laminating machine.	Can learner use a laminating machine?		4= laminates full length pages, small shapes, and irregularly shaped items and neatly trims excess lamination, 3= laminates full length pages, small shapes, and irregularly shaped items, 2= laminates full pages using lamination pouches, 1= turns on and identifies when laminator is ready for use	

The AFLS® - Vocational Skills Protocol

The Assessment of Functional Living Skills - The AFLS®

Office Skills (Continued)

TASK	SCORE	TASK NAME	TASK OBJECTIVE	QUESTION	EXAMPLE	CRITERIA	COMMENT
OF 17	0 1 2 3 4 0 1 2 3 4 0 1 2 3 4 0 1 2 3 4	Uses a fax machine	Learner will fax documents.	Can learner fax documents?		4= sends fax and prints confirmation, resends fax if transmission fails, checks destination fax number to ensure accuracy if failure occurs, 3= sends fax and prints confirmation, 2= loads papers, enters fax number, and sends fax, 1= loads papers into fax machine with correct orientation	

Mailing skills

TASK	SCORE	TASK NAME	TASK OBJECTIVE	QUESTION	EXAMPLE	CRITERIA	COMMENT
OF 18	0 1 2 0 1 2 0 1 2 0 1 2	Opens letters and packages	Learner will open letters, and packages without damaging content.	Can learner open letters and packages without damaging content?		2= opens letters and packages without damaging content, 1= opens letters and packages without damaging contents with only verbal prompts	
OF 19	0 1 2 0 1 2 0 1 2 0 1 2	Stuffs envelopes	Learner will stuff envelopes.	Can learner stuff envelopes?		2= arranges folded papers to align with addressee window (if present), licks or pulls adhesive strip from flap, and neatly seals flap, 1= folds sheets of paper neatly in thirds to fit into envelope	
OF 20	0 1 2 0 1 2 0 1 2 0 1 2	Places pre-printed address labels on envelopes	Learner will neatly place pre-printed address labels on envelopes.	Can learner place pre-printed address labels on envelopes neatly and in the correct position?		2= neatly places pre-printed address labels on envelopes in correct locations, 1= requires only verbal prompts to neatly place pre-printed address labels in correct locations	
OF 21	0 1 2 0 1 2 0 1 2 0 1 2	Addresses envelopes	Learner will address envelopes.	Can learner address envelopes?		2= hand writes address and return address on envelope or uses computer to print address and return address on envelope, 1= hand writes address and return address on envelope or uses computer to print address and return address on envelope with only verbal prompts	
OF 22	0 1 2 0 1 2 0 1 2 0 1 2	Distributes mail	Learner will distribute mail.	Can learner distribute mail?		2= sorts and delivers mail to multiple offices, 1= sorts mail into individual mailboxes	

The AFLS® - Vocational Skills Protocol

Office Skills (Continued)

TASK	SCORE	TASK NAME	TASK OBJECTIVE	QUESTION	EXAMPLE	CRITERIA	COMMENT
OF 23	0 1 2 0 1 2 0 1 2 0 1 2	Packs products into shipping containers	Learner will pack products into shipping containers.	Can learner pack products into shipping containers?	Smaller box, padded envelope, priority mail box, etc.	2= decides appropriate packaging for different products and sizes of items to be shipped, places item in packaging, adds filler or padding as needed, and seals, 1= places item into packaging given by someone else	
OF 24	0 1 2 0 1 2 0 1 2 0 1 2	Determines if letters need more than one stamp	Learner will decide whether envelope needs more than 1 stamp.	Can learner decide whether envelope may need more than 1 stamp?	Decides whether an envelope may weigh more than 1 ounce and might need an additional stamp	2= decides whether envelope feels too heavy and might need more than 1 stamp, 1= decides whether envelope feels too heavy and might need additional postage with assistance from supervisor	
OF 25	0 1 2 0 1 2 0 1 2 0 1 2	Adds postage using postage meter	Learner will use postage meter to determine postage for mail.	Can learner use a postage meter?		2= uses postage meter to determine postage for any domestic or international address, 1= uses postage meter to determine postage for any domestic address	
OF 26	0 1 2 0 1 2 0 1 2 0 1 2	Uses tracking and additional shipping options	Learner will ship using tracking and additional shipping options.	Can learner ship using tracking and additional shipping options?	Tracking, delivery confirmation, signature requirement, additional insurance, overnight delivery etc.	2= based on circumstances and immediate need, decides which shipping options to use, 1= when told which shipping options are necessary, ships using those options	
OF 27	0 1 2 0 1 2 0 1 2 0 1 2	Signs for packages	Learner will sign for packages.	Can learner sign for packages?		2= signs for packaging and places package in secure location or gives to trusted person, 1= signs for package under supervision	

Filing system skills

TASK	SCORE	TASK NAME	TASK OBJECTIVE	QUESTION	EXAMPLE	CRITERIA	COMMENT
OF 28	0 1 2 3 4 0 1 2 3 4 0 1 2 3 4 0 1 2 3 4	Sorts by numerical order	Learner will put items in numerical order.	Can learner put items in numerical order?		4= sorts by numerical order any number including decimals, 3= sorts any whole numbers up to 100, 2= sorts any whole numbers by numerical order up to 50, 1= sorts any whole number by numerical order up to 10	
OF 29	0 1 2 3 4 0 1 2 3 4 0 1 2 3 4 0 1 2 3 4	Alphabetizes	Learner will alphabetize.	Can learner alphabetize?	Spreadsheets, folders, business contacts, employee list, customer lists, sales leads, etc.	4= alphabetizes any names or words and places in alphabetical order by last, then first name, 3= alphabetizes using first 3 letters of word, 2= alphabetizes using only first 2 letters of word, 1= alphabetizes using only the first letter of word	

Office Skills (Continued)

TASK	SCORE	TASK NAME	TASK OBJECTIVE	QUESTION	EXAMPLE	CRITERIA	COMMENT
OF 30	0 1 2 0 1 2 0 1 2 0 1 2	Labels file folders	Learner will label file folders.	Can learner label file folders?	Writes heading onto top of manila file folders	2= labels file folders, 1= labels file folders when told what to write/type	
OF 31	0 1 2 0 1 2 0 1 2 0 1 2	Creates new hanging file folders	Learner will create new hanging file folders.	Can learner create new hanging file folders?	Labels insert, places insert into plastic tab, fits plastic tab into top of hanging file folder	2= creates new green hanging file folders, 1= creates new green hanging file folders with only verbal prompts	
OF 32	0 1 2 3 4 0 1 2 3 4 0 1 2 3 4 0 1 2 3 4	Uses filing cabinets	Learner will insert specific documents into folders, and retrieve and return file folders to specific locations in filing cabinet.	Can learner retrieve and return file folders?		4= retrieves and returns file folders, and inserts specific documents into folders in a filing cabinet with multiple drawers, 3= removes correct file folder and inserts a document and replaces in a single filing drawer, 2= correctly places a folder in a single file drawer, 1= retrieves a specified file folder from a single filing cabinet drawer	

Inventory management skills

TASK	SCORE	TASK NAME	TASK OBJECTIVE	QUESTION	EXAMPLE	CRITERIA	COMMENT
OF 33	0 1 2 3 4 0 1 2 3 4 0 1 2 3 4 0 1 2 3 4	Counts up to 100 items	Learner will count up to 100 items.	Can learner count up to 100 items?		4= counts up to 100 items, 3= counts up to 50 items, 2= counts up to 10 items, 1= counts up to 5 items	
OF 34	0 1 2 3 4 0 1 2 3 4 0 1 2 3 4 0 1 2 3 4	Counts inventory	Learner will take inventory count.	Can learner take inventory?	Counts inventory including labeled quantities of boxed items and loose items	4= takes inventory of at least 5 items with at least 20 pieces per item type, 3= takes inventory of at least 3 item types with at least 10 pieces per item type, 2= takes inventory of single item type with at least 10 pieces 1= takes inventory count of single item type containing fewer than 10 pieces	
OF 35	0 1 2 0 1 2 0 1 2 0 1 2	Orders supplies	Learner will order supplies.	Can learner order supplies?	Goes online and orders list of supplies learner generated, calls supply company to order list given to learner by supervisor	2= determines list of supplies that are in short supply and orders correct amount from distributor, 1= orders supplies from list given to learner by supervisor	

The Assessment of Functional Living Skills - The AFLS®

Office Skills (Continued)

Phone skills and responding to customer inquiries

TASK	SCORE	TASK NAME	TASK OBJECTIVE	QUESTION	EXAMPLE	CRITERIA	COMMENT
OF 36	0 1 2 3 4 0 1 2 3 4 0 1 2 3 4 0 1 2 3 4	Answers phones	Learner will answer phones including using appropriate voice qualities, taking written messages, transferring calls, and delivering messages.	Can learner answer phones?	Voice quality includes tone, clarity, volume, and rate of speech, in addition to manners, politeness, etc.	4= using appropriate voice qualities, answers phone, takes written messages, transfers calls to voicemail, transfers calls to employee extensions, delivers messages to correct person, 3= using appropriate voice qualities, answers phone, takes written messages and delivers messages to correct person, 2= answers phone and takes message, 1= answers phone, identifies who call should be directed to	
OF 37	0 1 2 3 4 0 1 2 3 4 0 1 2 3 4 0 1 2 3 4	Provides answers to customer inquiries	Learner will provide answers to customer inquiries.	Can learner provide answers to customer inquiries?	Provides answers to customer inquiries about product sales, hours, location, directions, returns, shipping information, etc.	4= in a professional manner, either on phone or in person provides answers to standard and non-standard customer inquiries, 3= answers standard or routine questions and identifies non-standard questions that need to be redirected to obtain answers, obtains customer contact information so they can be contacted later with answer to inquiry, 2= answers standard or routine questions and identifies non-standard questions that need to be redirected to obtain answers, 1= answers standard or routine questions	
OF 38	0 1 2 0 1 2 0 1 2 0 1 2	Provides answers to customer inquiries by email	Learner will provide answers to customer inquiries by email.	Can learner provide answers to customer inquiries by email?		2= independently obtains information to answer email inquiries professionally and in a timely manner, 1= requires oversight prior to sending email response to ensure accuracy	

The AFLS® - Vocational Skills Protocol

Copyright © 2015 by Behavior Analysts, Inc. and Stimulus Publications
ALL RIGHTS RESERVED

The Assessment of Functional Living Skills - The AFLS®

Office Skills (Continued)

Confidentiality issues

TASK	SCORE	TASK NAME	TASK OBJECTIVE	QUESTION	EXAMPLE	CRITERIA	COMMENT
OF 39	0 1 2 3 4 0 1 2 3 4 0 1 2 3 4 0 1 2 3 4	Identifies, stores, and disposes of confidential information	Learner will Identify confidential information that must be kept private and shredded when no longer needed.	Can learner Identifying confidential information that must be kept private and shredded when no longer needed?	Removes and shreds documents containing personal information before putting remaining file into recycling bin	4= recognizes paperwork that contains private or confidential information and shreds those documents when they are no longer needed, 3= requires assistance in determining whether papers containing confidential information are still needed before shredding, 2= recognizes paperwork that contains private or confidential information and shreds those documents when told to do so, 1= recognizes paperwork that contains private or confidential information and understands the need for protecting the information	NEEDS CLOSE SUPERVISION
OF 40	0 1 2 0 1 2 0 1 2 0 1 2	Maintains confidentiality of information	Learner will maintain confidentiality of private information that is seen in documents, is told to learner, or is overheard being discussed by others.	Does learner maintain confidentiality of private information that is seen in documents, is told to learner, or is overheard being discussed by others?	Covers up or turns over paper documents containing private information, locks in cabinet, etc.	2= recognizes individuals who should and should not be provided with certain information and maintains the confidentiality of that information, 1= keeps information to self when told is not supposed to share information with others	NEEDS CLOSE SUPERVISION

The AFLS® - Vocational Skills Protocol

The Assessment of Functional Living Skills - The AFLS®

Computer Skills

TASK	SCORE	TASK NAME	TASK OBJECTIVE	QUESTION	EXAMPLE	CRITERIA	COMMENT
CP 1	0 1 2 0 1 2 0 1 2 0 1 2	Turns on computer	Learner will turn on a computer and monitor.	Does learner turn on computer and monitor?	Desktop computer with separate monitor	2= turns on and off computer and monitor, 1= turns on computer and monitor with only verbal prompts	
CP 2	0 1 2 3 4 0 1 2 3 4 0 1 2 3 4 0 1 2 3 4	Operates cursor using a mouse	Learner will operate a computer mouse.	Does learner use a mouse to control a computer?		4= controls cursor with mouse to move/open windows or icons, click on objects or buttons, and access pull-down menus, 3= controls cursor with mouse to move open windows or icons and click on objects or buttons, 2= requires only verbal prompts to navigate to and click on objects or buttons on the screen, 1= requires model prompts or slight physical prompts to navigate and to click on objects or buttons	
CP 3	0 1 2 3 4 0 1 2 3 4 0 1 2 3 4 0 1 2 3 4	Moves cursor using fingers	Learner will move computer cursor using finger controls.	Can learner operate cursor with finger controls?	Finger pad on laptops and electronic tablets	4= uses fingers on cursor to move or open windows or icons, clicks on objects or buttons, and accesses pull-down menus, 3= uses fingers to move cursor to open windows or icons and clicks on objects or buttons, 2= requires only verbal prompts to use fingers to navigate to and click on objects or buttons on the screen, 1= requires model prompts or slight physical prompts to use fingers to navigate and click on objects or buttons	
CP 4	0 1 2 3 4 0 1 2 3 4 0 1 2 3 4 0 1 2 3 4	Logs onto and off computer	Learner will log onto and off of computers.	Does learner log on and off computers?		4 = consistently logs onto computers or password protected websites using multiple user name and password combinations and consistently logs off when finished, 3 = consistently logs onto computers or password protected websites using a single user name and password combination and consistently logs off when finished, 2= consistently logs onto computers or password protected websites using single user name and password combination but does not consistently log off when finished, 1= requires verbal prompts to log onto computers or password protected sites	

The AFLS® - Vocational Skills Protocol

The Assessment of Functional Living Skills - The AFLS®

Computer Skills (Continued)

TASK	SCORE	TASK NAME	TASK OBJECTIVE	QUESTION	EXAMPLE	CRITERIA	COMMENT
CP 5	0 1 2 0 1 2 0 1 2 0 1 2	Waits during progress bar, hour glass etc.	Learner will wait to manipulate computer controls when progress bar, hour glass, etc. is signaling that computer is completing a task.	Does learner wait to operate computer while progress bar is present?		2= waits when progress bar or other task indicator is present, 1= requires verbal prompts to wait when progress bar or indicator is present	
CP 6	0 1 2 3 4 0 1 2 3 4 0 1 2 3 4 0 1 2 3 4	Starts and saves a new document	Learner will start and save a new document.	Can learner start and save a new document?		4= opens appropriate program, creates a new document, and saves and closes documents, 3= opens, saves, and closes an existing document, 2= requires only verbal prompts to open, save, and close an existing document, 1= requires only verbal prompts to save an existing open document	
CP 7	0 1 2 0 1 2 0 1 2 0 1 2	Saves a revised copy of a document as a new document	Learner will save a revised copy of a document as a new document.	Can learner save a revised copy of a document as a new document?		2= after making changes to a document, saves the document as a new document (save as), 1= requires only verbal prompts to save changed document as a new document	
CP 8	0 1 2 3 4 0 1 2 3 4 0 1 2 3 4 0 1 2 3 4	Formats a document	Learner will format a document.	Can learner format a document?		4= makes changes to page orientation, margins and percent of enlargement or reduction of page, 3= makes changes to page orientation and margins, 2= changes page orientation, but requires verbal prompts to make changes to margins, 1= requires only verbal prompts to change page orientation (landscape or portrait)	
CP 9	0 1 2 3 4 0 1 2 3 4 0 1 2 3 4 0 1 2 3 4	Changes font features	Learner will change common font features in a document.	Can learner change common font features such as size and color in a document?	Font type, font color, font size, justification (left, center, or right), bold, underline, italics, highlight, etc.	4= makes changes to 6 common font features, 3= makes changes to 4 common font features, 2= makes changes to 2 common font features, 1= requires verbal prompts to make a change to a common font feature	

The AFLS® - Vocational Skills Protocol

The Assessment of Functional Living Skills - The AFLS®

Computer Skills (Continued)

TASK	SCORE	TASK NAME	TASK OBJECTIVE	QUESTION	EXAMPLE	CRITERIA	COMMENT
CP 10	0 1 2 3 4 0 1 2 3 4 0 1 2 3 4 0 1 2 3 4	Highlights, copies, cuts, and pastes in document	Learner will highlight, copy, cut, and paste in a document.	Can learner highlight, copy, cut, and paste in a document?		4= highlights segments of text, pictures, and objects and cuts, copies, and pastes using both keyboard **and** pull-down menus, 3= highlights segments of text, pictures, and objects and cuts, copies, and pastes using **either** keyboard **or** pull-down menus, 2= highlights text, pictures, and objects but requires verbal prompts to cut, copy, and paste, 1= requires verbal prompts to highlight objects or text	
CP 11	0 1 2 0 1 2 0 1 2 0 1 2	Spell checks	Learner will use spell check feature in computer to check spelling of words in documents.	Does learner use spell check to ensure correct spelling after typing?		2= spell checks documents, 1= requires only verbal prompts to spell check documents	
CP 12	0 1 2 3 4 0 1 2 3 4 0 1 2 3 4 0 1 2 3 4	Makes and uses folders	Learner will make, label and use folders on desktop or other storage location.	Can learner make and use folders to organize data?		4= makes, labels, and uses folders to keep all data organized and easy to find, 3= makes folders but requires verbal prompts to label or use them for organization, 2= requires verbal prompts to make and label folders, 1= requires model prompts or slight physical prompts to make and label folders	
CP 13	0 1 2 0 1 2 0 1 2 0 1 2	Schedules events on computer	Learner will schedule events on computer calendar.	Can learner schedule events on a computer calendar?		2= using a shared computerized calendar system, schedules variety of tasks for multiple people, 1= using a computerized calendar system, schedules variety of tasks for self	
CP 14	0 1 2 3 4 0 1 2 3 4 0 1 2 3 4 0 1 2 3 4	Opens a computer program	Learner will open a computer program from the desktop and from the computer's main list.	Does learner open computer programs?		4= opens a computer program from desktop icon and from the computers main list of programs, 3= opens a program from the desktop icon, 2= requires only verbal prompts to open a program from desktop icon, 1= requires model or slight physical prompts to open a program from desktop icon	
CP 15	0 1 2 3 4 0 1 2 3 4 0 1 2 3 4 0 1 2 3 4	Operates DVD drive	Learner will insert a DVD into a computer and play DVDs.	Can learner insert and play a DVD in a computer?		4= inserts and presses play to start watching a DVD, and pauses, rewinds, and selects chapters to watch on a DVD, 3= inserts and presses play to start watching a DVD, 2= requires only verbal prompts to insert and play a DVD, 1= requires model or slight physical prompts to insert and play a DVD	

Computer Skills (Continued)

TASK	SCORE	TASK NAME	TASK OBJECTIVE	QUESTION	EXAMPLE	CRITERIA	COMMENT
CP 16	0 1 2 3 4 0 1 2 3 4 0 1 2 3 4 0 1 2 3 4	Identifies which program is needed for specific tasks	Learner will identify which program is needed for specific tasks.	Does learner identify which program is used for specific tasks?	Word processing for writing a letter, spreadsheet program for calculations and for making graphs, drawing program for making illustrations, photo editing program for pictures, email program for correspondence, etc.	4= identifies at least 5 different programs for different tasks, 3= 4 programs, 2= 3 programs, 1= identifies at least 2 different programs for different tasks	
CP 17	0 1 2 0 1 2 0 1 2 0 1 2	Prints various content	Learner will print a document, online content, and pictures.	Can learner print a document, online content, and pictures?		2= prints various documents by choosing printer, selecting page range and number of copies, 1= prints a document by "quick print" icon on tool bar	
CP 18	0 1 2 3 4 0 1 2 3 4 0 1 2 3 4 0 1 2 3 4	Operates CD-ROM	Learner will insert a blank CD disc into a computer and copy documents to and from the disc.	Can learner insert a CD disc into a computer and copy documents to and from the disc?		4= stores **and** retrieves information from a CD disc, 3= stores **or** retrieves information from a CD disc, 2= requires only verbal prompts to store or retrieve data from a CD disc, 1= requires a model or slight physical prompts to store or retrieve data from a CD disc	
CP 19	0 1 2 0 1 2 0 1 2 0 1 2	Types sentences using appropriate finger position	Learner will type sentences using appropriate finger positions.	Does learner type sentences using appropriate finger positions?		2= types sentences using correct finger positions on "qwerty" keyboard, 1= types words but not using correct finger position on keyboard	
CP 20	0 1 2 3 4 0 1 2 3 4 0 1 2 3 4 0 1 2 3 4	Uses search engines	Learner will search for topics using a search engine.	Can learner search for topics using a search engine?	Pudding, rice pudding, dessert recipes that use rice, video of how to make rice pudding, etc.	4= uses search engine effectively to search for multiple-word descriptors to locate text, pictures, and videos of desired topics, 3= uses search engine to search for one-word topics, 2= requires only verbal prompts to navigate to search engine and search for topics, 1= requires model or slight physical prompts to navigate to and use search engine	
CP 21	0 1 2 0 1 2 0 1 2 0 1 2	Safeguards usernames and passwords	Learner will use a system to remember and maintain security of usernames and passwords for computers and other electronic devices.	Does learner use a system to remember and maintain security of usernames and passwords for computers and other electronic devices?	Keeps usernames and passwords in written form in safe place	2= creates, changes, remembers, and maintains security of user names and passwords, 1= maintains security of user names and passwords	NEEDS CLOSE SUPERVISION

The AFLS® - Vocational Skills Protocol

The Assessment of Functional Living Skills - The AFLS®

Computer Skills (Continued)

TASK	SCORE	TASK NAME	TASK OBJECTIVE	QUESTION	EXAMPLE	CRITERIA	COMMENT
CP 22	0 1 2 3 4 0 1 2 3 4 0 1 2 3 4 0 1 2 3 4	Backs up computer data	Learner will describe how to back up data and why it is important, and will back up data on a regular basis.	Does learner back up computer data?		4= describes how to back up data, and why it is important, and backs up all data regularly, 3= backs up some data on regular basis, 2= requires verbal prompts to back up data, 1= requires model or slight physical prompt to back up data	
CP 23	0 1 2 3 4 0 1 2 3 4 0 1 2 3 4 0 1 2 3 4	Uses a portable drive	Learner will insert a portable drive into a computer and copy items to and from a flash drive.	Can learner insert a portable drive into a computer and copy items to and from drive?		4= describes how to save data to a portable drive and stores and retrieves information from the drive, 3= stores and retrieves data from the drive, 2= requires only verbal prompts to store and retrieve data from the drive, 1= requires model or slight physical prompts to store or retrieve data from the drive	
CP 24	0 1 2 0 1 2 0 1 2 0 1 2	Searches for files	Learner will use the computer's search function to find specific documents on the computer.	Can learner search the computer to locate specific files?		2= uses the computer's search program to locate specific computer files, 1= when provided with only verbal prompts, uses the computer's search program to locate specific computer files	
CP 25	0 1 2 3 4 0 1 2 3 4 0 1 2 3 4 0 1 2 3 4	Operates laptop computer	Learner will use laptop computer to run programs and applications, save documents, and transfer files to an external storage device.	Can learner operate a laptop computer?		4= turns on and off, uses at least 3 programs and applications, internally saves documents and transfers files to other external storage devices, 3= turns on and off and uses at least 2 programs and applications on a laptop computer, 2= turns on and off a laptop computer, 1= requires only verbal prompts to turn on and off a laptop computer	
CP 26	0 1 2 0 1 2 0 1 2 0 1 2	Ensures laptop safety	Learner will take reasonable precautions to ensure laptop safety.	Does learner keep laptop safe?	Keeps laptop in case, gentle with keyboard, does not drop laptop, takes reasonable precautions to keep laptop away from liquids or edges or tables, etc.	2= maintains secure possession of laptop, carries it in a padded case, handles laptop in a gentle manner, and always places it on stable surface that is in a hazard-free location, 1= requires only verbal prompts to handle laptop in a gentle manner and to place it on a stable surface that is in a hazard-free location	

The AFLS® - Vocational Skills Protocol

The Assessment of Functional Living Skills - The AFLS®

Computer Skills (Continued)

TASK	SCORE	TASK NAME	TASK OBJECTIVE	QUESTION	EXAMPLE	CRITERIA	COMMENT
CP 27	0 1 2 3 4 0 1 2 3 4 0 1 2 3 4 0 1 2 3 4	Monitors laptop battery charge	Learner will monitor and maintain a fully-charged laptop battery.	Does learner maintain sufficient battery life on laptop or tablet?		4= identifies high and low battery life indicator lights, plugs device into outlet to maintain adequate battery charge, 3= identifies battery life indicator lights but requires verbal prompts to check "remaining battery charge" to determine if learner needs to plug laptop into an outlet, 2= locates the "remaining battery charge" indicator, 1= plugs device laptop computer into outlet	
CP 28	0 1 2 3 4 0 1 2 3 4 0 1 2 3 4 0 1 2 3 4	Uses spreadsheet programs	Learner will use spreadsheet programs.	Can learner use spreadsheet programs?		4= opens, creates new spreadsheet, enters data, and saves, 3= opens an existing document, enters data, and saves, 2= opens an existing document, but requires verbal prompts to enter data and save, 1= requires only verbal prompts to open spreadsheet program	
CP 29	0 1 2 0 1 2 0 1 2 0 1 2	Completes computerized forms	Learner will enter data into computerized forms.	Can learner enter data into computerized forms?	Customer information into company database, sales reports, inventory received, employee hours and days worked, etc.	2= enters data into a variety of online and computerized company forms, 1= enters data into at least 1 computerized form	
CP 30	0 1 2 3 4 0 1 2 3 4 0 1 2 3 4 0 1 2 3 4	Sends and receives email	Learner will read and send email.	Does learner communicate with others using email?	For acceptable school assignments, academic activities, and teacher requests	4= sends, receives, replies to, saves, and deletes emails, and adds new contacts to email program, 3= sends, receives, and replies to emails, and adds new contacts to email program, 2= sends, receives, and replies to emails, and when provided with only verbal prompts, adds new contacts to email program, 1= when provided with only verbal prompts, sends, receives, and replies to emails	NEEDS CLOSE SUPERVISION
CP 31	0 1 2 3 4 0 1 2 3 4 0 1 2 3 4 0 1 2 3 4	Uses online map websites to obtain directions	Learner will obtain directions between locations using an online mapping site.	Can learner find directions between locations using an online mapping site?	MapQuest, Google Maps, etc.	4= finds directions between 2 locations, finds own home, finds a given address, and finds known landmarks using mapping website, 3= finds directions between 2 locations, and finds own home using mapping website, 2= finds own address, 1= requires verbal prompts to find a location on a mapping website	

The AFLS® - Vocational Skills Protocol

The Assessment of Functional Living Skills - The AFLS®

Restaurant Skills

Bussing tables and washing dishes

TASK	SCORE	TASK NAME	TASK OBJECTIVE	QUESTION	EXAMPLE	CRITERIA	COMMENT
RS 1	0 1 2 3 4 0 1 2 3 4 0 1 2 3 4 0 1 2 3 4	Cleans tables and chairs	Learner will clean tables and chairs.	Can learner clean tables and chairs?		4= wipes loose debris into trash, sprays table and wipes so no spots or food residue is present, dries table, sprays cleaning solution into chairs, cleans and dries chairs as needed, 3= wipes loose debris into trash, sprays table and wipes so no spots or food residue is present, dries table, 2= wipes table free of loose debris, 1= requires verbal prompts to wipe table free of loose debris	
RS 2	0 1 2 0 1 2 0 1 2 0 1 2	Buses tables	Learner will bus tables.	Can learner bus tables?		2= places all plates, cups, silverware, and other service items into bus tray and carries away without dropping or spilling, 1= requires verbal prompts to places plates, cups, silverware, and other service items into bus tray to minimize spilling	
RS 3	0 1 2 0 1 2 0 1 2 0 1 2	Sanitizes tables, counter, and chairs	Learner will sanitize tables, counter, and chairs.	Can learner sanitize tables, counter, and chairs?		2= applies sanitizer to cloth or directly to surface and wipes all surfaces that might come into contact with customers, 1= applies sanitizer to cloth or directly to surface and wipes all surfaces that might come into contact with customers with only verbal prompts	
RS 4	0 1 2 0 1 2 0 1 2 0 1 2	Scrapes and rinses dishes to be washed	Learner will scrape and rinse dishes to be washed.	Can learner scrape and rinse dishes to be washed?	Takes plate of food and trash, scrapes into garbage without throwing away any silverware	2= scrapes food and garbage into trash, rinses food residue from dishes without throwing away silverware, 1= scrapes food and garbage from dishes into trash with only verbal prompts	
RS 5	0 1 2 3 4 0 1 2 3 4 0 1 2 3 4 0 1 2 3 4	Puts dishes in dishwasher	Learner will place dishes, cups, and utensils in a dishwasher.	Does learner place all dishes, cups, and utensils in a dishwasher?	Learner loads all plates, bowls, cups, and silverware into a dishwasher	4= finds appropriate locations and places all dishes, cups, and utensils in dishwasher using both the bottom and top dish racks, 3= finds appropriate placements for plates, bowls, cups, and silverware with only verbal prompts, 2= places plates and silverware in dishwasher, 1= places plates and silverware with only verbal prompts	

The Assessment of Functional Living Skills - The AFLS®

Restaurant Skills (Continued)

TASK	SCORE	TASK NAME	TASK OBJECTIVE	QUESTION	EXAMPLE	CRITERIA	COMMENT
RS 6	0 1 2 3 4 0 1 2 3 4 0 1 2 3 4 0 1 2 3 4	Operates dishwasher	Learner will operate dishwasher.	Does learner operate dishwasher?	Puts in detergent, sets the dials to appropriate settings, turns on the dishwasher	4= adds detergent, closes door, sets the control settings, and turns on dishwasher, 3= adds detergent, closes door, sets the control settings with only verbal prompts, and turns on dishwasher, 2= adds detergent, closes door, and turns on dishwasher with only verbal prompts, 1= adds dishwasher detergent, closes door and turns on dishwasher with only minimal physical prompts	
RS 7	0 1 2 3 4 0 1 2 3 4 0 1 2 3 4 0 1 2 3 4	Unloads dishwasher	Learner will unload all glasses, silverware, dishes, and pots from top and bottom rack and puts away in appropriate locations.	Does learner unload the dishwasher?		4= unloads all glasses, silverware, dishes, and pots from top and bottom rack and places in appropriate locations, 3= requires only verbal prompts to remove plates, glasses, and silverware and put in correct locations, 2= removes plates, glasses, and silverware and gives to caregiver upon request, 1= removes plates and glasses from dishwasher and gives to caregiver upon request	
RS 8	0 1 2 3 4 0 1 2 3 4 0 1 2 3 4 0 1 2 3 4	Hand-washes dishes and utensils	Learner will hand-wash dishes and utensils.	Can learner hand-wash dishes and utensils?		4= soaks pans if required to soften baked on food, washes all dishes, glasses, and utensils thoroughly, 3= soaks pans if directed to in order to soften baked on food, washes all dishes, glasses, and utensils thoroughly, 2= washes dishes and pans independently, requires verbal prompts to wash glasses and utensils, 1= washes dishes and pans that do not contain baked on food	NEEDS CLOSE SUPERVISION
RS 9	0 1 2 0 1 2 0 1 2 0 1 2	Cleans bins used to bus tables	Learner will clean bins used to bus tables.	Can learner clean bins used to bus tables?		2= washes bus trays/bins, 1= requires verbal prompts to wash bus trays/bins	
RS 10	0 1 2 0 1 2 0 1 2 0 1 2	Sorts silverware	Learner will sort all spoons, forks, and knives into correct trays.	Does learner sort silverware?	Places large forks with other large forks, teaspoons with teaspoons, etc.	2= sorts all spoons, forks, and knives into correct trays, 1= sorts silverware with only verbal prompts	NEEDS CLOSE SUPERVISION

The AFLS® - Vocational Skills Protocol

The Assessment of Functional Living Skills - The AFLS®

Restaurant Skills (Continued)

Restaurant upkeep

TASK	SCORE	TASK NAME	TASK OBJECTIVE	QUESTION	EXAMPLE	CRITERIA	COMMENT
RS 11	0 1 2 0 1 2 0 1 2 0 1 2	Wraps silverware into napkins	Learner will wrap silverware into napkins.	Can learner wrap silverware into napkins?		2 = neatly wraps or folds napkins around silverware and binds with sticker tape or band, 1= neatly wraps or folds napkins around silverware and binds with sticker tape or band with only verbal prompts	NEEDS CLOSE SUPERVISION
RS 12	0 1 2 3 4 0 1 2 3 4 0 1 2 3 4 0 1 2 3 4	Refills napkin holders	Learner will refill napkin holders.	Does learner refill napkin holders?	Learner checks tables and refills napkin holders being careful not to overfill them	4= checks napkin holders, obtains napkins from storage, replenishes when low, 3= checks napkin holders, obtains napkins from storage, replenishes when told to do so, 2= when given a supply of napkins, replenishes when told to, 1= when given a supply of napkins, replenishes when told to, with only verbal prompts	
RS 13	0 1 2 3 4 0 1 2 3 4 0 1 2 3 4 0 1 2 3 4	Replenishes packets of condiment items	Learner will replenish condiment packets into table-top containers as needed to maintain useable supply.	Can learner replenish condiment packets?	Sugar, creamer, salt, pepper, hot sauce packets, etc.	4= independently checks condiment holders, obtains required condiments from storage, replenishes when low, 3= checks condiment holders, obtains required condiments from storage, replenishes when told to do so, 2= when given a supply of condiments, replenishes when told to, 1= when given a supply of condiments, replenishes when told to, with only verbal prompts	
RS 14	0 1 2 0 1 2 0 1 2 0 1 2	Refills condiment and salt and pepper containers	Learner will refill condiment and salt and pepper containers.	Does learner refill condiment and salt and pepper containers?	Ketchup, mustard, soy sauce, sugar, syrup, salt and pepper, etc.	2= checks containers to determine if refill is required, refills condiment containers without spilling, or if spills, cleans spilled materials and container, 1= requires verbal prompts to refill containers	
RS 15	0 1 2 0 1 2 0 1 2 0 1 2	Puts out plates and silverware for self service	Learner will put out plates and silverware for self service.	Can learner put out plates and silverware for self service?		2= monitors levels to ensure quantity is sufficient for demand, stacks cups, bowls, plates in correct locations, and places silverware into correct containers (all items needed for situation) to allow customer to obtain in self-service, 1= stacks cups, bowls, plates in correct locations, and places silverware into correct containers (all items needed for situation) to allow customer to obtain in self-service	NEEDS CLOSE SUPERVISION

The AFLS® - Vocational Skills Protocol

The Assessment of Functional Living Skills - The AFLS®

Restaurant Skills (Continued)

TASK	SCORE	TASK NAME	TASK OBJECTIVE	QUESTION	EXAMPLE	CRITERIA	COMMENT
RS 16	0 1 2 3 4 0 1 2 3 4 0 1 2 3 4 0 1 2 3 4	Sets tables	Learner will set tables.	Can learner set tables?		4= adds additional or removes existing place settings to accommodate a change in the number of seated guests, 3= places all silverware, plates, cups, saucers, glasses, napkins, and all related service items and condiments in correct location on table for as many settings as are required for table size, 2= places all silverware, plates, cups, saucers, glasses, napkins, in correct location on table for 2 settings, 1= sets one table setting with verbal prompts	NEEDS CLOSE SUPERVISION

Food handling and preparation

TASK	SCORE	TASK NAME	TASK OBJECTIVE	QUESTION	EXAMPLE	CRITERIA	COMMENT
RS 17	0 1 2 0 1 2 0 1 2 0 1 2	Refills cold beverages	Learner will circulate around customers and refill cold beverages as needed.	Can learner circulate and refill cold drinks?	Sweet tea, water, soda, etc.	2= walks around seating area scanning for cold beverages that need to be refilled, approaches and asks if customer wants refill, 1= approaches and asks if customer wants refill when told who to approach	
RS 18	0 1 2 0 1 2 0 1 2 0 1 2	Refills hot beverages	Learner will circulate around customers and refill hot beverages as needed.	Can learner refill hot beverages?	Coffee, hot tea, etc.	2= walks around seating area scanning for hot beverages that need to be refilled, approaches and asks if customer wants refill, 1= approaches and asks if customer wants refill when told who to approach	NEEDS CLOSE SUPERVISION
RS 19	0 1 2 0 1 2 0 1 2 0 1 2	Serves meals	Learner will serve food to customers by carrying plates and glasses to tables.	Can learner carry plates and glasses to tables?		2= carries tray of plates and drinks to table, sets up serving stand, places plates and glasses in appropriate place by person who ordered food, 1= follows instructions to carry at least 2 items to table and delivers to correct person	
RS 20	0 1 2 0 1 2 0 1 2 0 1 2	Wraps food prior to storage	Learner will wrap food prior to storing.	Can learner wrap food?		2= chooses correct type of wrap and applies wrap tightly around bowl or food item, 1= requires only verbal prompts to wrap food or dish	

The AFLS® - Vocational Skills Protocol

The Assessment of Functional Living Skills - The AFLS®

Restaurant Skills (Continued)

TASK	SCORE	TASK NAME	TASK OBJECTIVE	QUESTION	EXAMPLE	CRITERIA	COMMENT
RS 21	0 1 2 0 1 2 0 1 2 0 1 2	Rotates stock of food items	Learner will rotate stock of food items.	Can learner rotate stock of food items?		2= selects items with the expiration date closest to present and places in front of stock with later dates, 1= selects items with the expiration date closest to present and places in front of stock with later dates with only verbal prompts	
RS 22	0 1 2 0 1 2 0 1 2 0 1 2	Organizes food items and supplies	Learner will organize food items supplies.	Can learner organize food items and supplies?	Sorts, stacks, puts items in correct location, etc.	2= organizes food items and supplies in pantry, refrigerator, and freezer, 1= requires verbal prompts to organize food and supplies	
RS 23	0 1 2 3 4 0 1 2 3 4 0 1 2 3 4 0 1 2 3 4	Refills food items in a salad bar or buffet	Learner will refill food items in a salad bar or buffet.	Can learner refill food items in a salad bar or buffet?	Tray of lasagna runs low, learner replaces with new tray, learner sees that lettuce is low and brings out a bowl of lettuce to add to bowl in buffet	4= determines when items need to be replaced, replaces all solid and liquid food items or trays, cleans areas around food items when replacing, carries items into kitchen, 3= when directed to replenish items, replaces all solid and liquid food items or trays, cleans areas around food items when replacing, carries items into kitchen, 2= places solid food items into appropriate locations, 1= carries replacement food items to buffet line and empty containers back to kitchen	
RS 24	0 1 2 0 1 2 0 1 2 0 1 2	Stores food	Learner will store food.	Can learner store food items in correct locations?		2= places food in correct location (refrigerator, freezer, pantry or storage room, 1= follows instructions to place food items in specific locations	
RS 25	0 1 2 3 4 0 1 2 3 4 0 1 2 3 4 0 1 2 3 4	Determines inedible food by smell, appearance, and passage of time	Learner will identify and discard spoiled refrigerated foods and liquids based on smell or appearance.	Does learner determine inedible food by smell, appearance, and passage of time?	Spoiled milk, fruits with brown spots, moldy bread, cheese or lunch meats, or cooked vegetables or meats that "smells bad," etc.	4= independently identifies and discards prepared refrigerated foods and fruits, vegetables, bread, and liquids based on smell or looks spoiled, 3= independently visually identifies and discards spoiled fruit and vegetables and moldy food items, 2= independently identifies at least 2 examples of fruits, vegetables or breads that are spoiled, 1= identifies at least 2 examples of fruits, vegetables or breads that are spoiled with only verbal prompts	

The AFLS® - Vocational Skills Protocol

The Assessment of Functional Living Skills - The AFLS®

Restaurant Skills (Continued)

TASK	SCORE	TASK NAME	TASK OBJECTIVE	QUESTION	EXAMPLE	CRITERIA	COMMENT
RS 26	0 1 2 0 1 2 0 1 2 0 1 2	Washes foods before cooking	Learner will wash food items and place them in a colander or drainer.	Does learner wash fruits and vegetables and other food items?		2= washes fruits and vegetables and places them in a colander or drainer, rinses seafood or other raw foods prior to cooking, 1= cleans fruits and vegetables and places them in a colander or drainer	

Wait staff

TASK	SCORE	TASK NAME	TASK OBJECTIVE	QUESTION	EXAMPLE	CRITERIA	COMMENT
RS 27	0 1 2 0 1 2 0 1 2 0 1 2	Seats customers	Learner will seat customers.	Can learner seat customers?		2= checks master list or computer for available seating and leads patrons to open seat, brings correct number of menus, kids menus, and crayons (if available), 1= leads customers to table as directed by supervisor or greeter	
RS 28	0 1 2 3 4 0 1 2 3 4 0 1 2 3 4 0 1 2 3 4	Takes customer orders	Learner will take orders from customers.	Can learner take orders from customers?	One person in the group orders a chicken sandwich with no cheese, and a wheat bun instead of a white bun	4= takes orders from parties of 4 or more people with items ordered that include substitutions or deletions from the typical menu, 3= takes orders from 2 people of at least 2 items each, 2= takes order from 1 person with no more than 3 items ordered, 1= takes order from 1 person with no more than 2 items ordered	
RS 29	0 1 2 0 1 2 0 1 2 0 1 2	Removes dirty dishes from tables as food is finished	Learner will remove dirty dishes from tables as food is finished.	Can learner remove dirty dishes from tables as food is finished?		2= walks around seating area scanning for dishes that are no longer needed at table, approaches and asks if customer wants dishes removed, removes unwanted items, 1= when told who to approach by supervisor, approaches and asks if customer wants dishes removed, removes unwanted items	
RS 30	0 1 2 0 1 2 0 1 2 0 1 2	Asks customers if they need anything	Learner will ask customers if they need anything.	Can learner ask customers if they need anything?		2= scan assigned tables, check to see if those customers need anything, retrieve and deliver what was needed, 1= requires verbal prompts to check with customers, independently retrieves and delivers wanted items	
RS 31	0 1 2 0 1 2 0 1 2 0 1 2	Responds to customers' requests	Learner will respond to customers' requests in satisfactory manner.	Can learner respond to customers' requests?		2= responds to customer requests and meets those requests, seeks supervisor in situations in which learner does not readily know how to meet request, 1= makes changes to initial order and informs customers of additional charges if any	

The AFLS® - Vocational Skills Protocol

Restaurant Skills (Continued)

TASK	SCORE	TASK NAME	TASK OBJECTIVE	QUESTION	EXAMPLE	CRITERIA	COMMENT
RS 32	0 1 2 0 1 2 0 1 2 0 1 2	Resolves customers problems or complaints	Learner will resolve customer's problems or complaints and seeks supervisor assistance when necessary.	Can learner resolve customer problems or complaints?		2= remains calm and reaches satisfactory resolution with customer complaints or politely retrieves supervisor and explains issue for supervisor to resolve, 1= retrieves supervisor when confronted with customer complaints	
RS 33	0 1 2 3 4 0 1 2 3 4 0 1 2 3 4 0 1 2 3 4	Place portions in "to go" containers	Learner will place portions in "to go" containers.	Can learner place portions in "to go" containers?		4= determines number and correct sizes of boxes, fills and closes boxes, 3= fills and closes with only verbal prompts, 2= identifies number, size and types of containers needed, 1= retrieves the number, size and types of containers requested	

The AFLS® - Vocational Skills Protocol

The Assessment of Functional Living Skills - The AFLS®

RESTAURANT   **RESTAURANT KITCHEN**

Restaurant Kitchen

Kitchen skills

TASK	SCORE	TASK NAME	TASK OBJECTIVE	QUESTION	EXAMPLE	CRITERIA	COMMENT
RK 1	0 1 2 0 1 2 0 1 2 0 1 2	Uses utensils	Learner will use at least 8 different kitchen utensils.	Can learner use a variety of utensils?	Cake server, salad spoons, tongs, spatula, ladle, pizza cutter, paring knife, orange peeler, cheese grater, cheese shredder, etc.	2= uses at least 8 different kitchen utensils safely, effectively, and as intended, 1= uses at least 4 different utensils safely, effectively, and as intended	NEEDS CLOSE SUPERVISION
RK 2	0 1 2 3 4 0 1 2 3 4 0 1 2 3 4 0 1 2 3 4	Cuts with knives	Learner will use 4 different methods to cut.	Can learner use different methods to cut?	Slice, peel, dice, chop, shred, trim, etc.	4= safely cuts with 4 different methods, 3= safely cuts 3 different methods, 2= slices and cuts food items into approximately the same size as a sample, 1= requires close supervision to cut items in half	NEEDS CLOSE SUPERVISION
RK 3	0 1 2 3 4 0 1 2 3 4 0 1 2 3 4 0 1 2 3 4	States abbreviations for standard measurements	Learner will state the measurement when shown their abbreviations.	Can learner identify abbreviations for standard measurements?	lbs., oz., tsp., tbsp., C., pt., qt., gal, etc.	4= states the measurement unit for at least 8 abbreviations, 3= states the measurement unit for at least 6 abbreviations, 2= states the measurement unit for at least 4 abbreviations, 1= states the measurement unit for at least 2 abbreviations	
RK 4	0 1 2 3 4 0 1 2 3 4 0 1 2 3 4 0 1 2 3 4	Measures weights	Learner will determine the weight of objects using ounces and pounds.	Can learner determine the weight of objects?	Ounces, pounds (or metric equivalents), etc.	4= measures and states the weight of an object to the nearest pound for up to 10 pounds, and to the nearest ounce for objects weighing less than a pound, 3= measures and states the weight of an object to the nearest pound for up to 10 pounds, or to the nearest ounce for objects weighing less than a pound, 2= measures and states the weight of an object to the nearest pound for up to 5 pounds, 1= when provided with only verbal prompts, measures and states the weight of an object to the nearest pound for up to 5 pounds	
RK 5	0 1 2 3 4 0 1 2 3 4 0 1 2 3 4 0 1 2 3 4	Measures liquid volume	Learner will measure liquid volumes of a cup, 1/2 cup, 1/3 cup, 1/4 cup, 1 tablespoon, and 1 teaspoon.	Does learner measure the volume of liquids?	Water, oil, etc.	4= measures liquids volumes of a cup, 1/2 cup, 1/3 cup, 1/4 cup, 1 tablespoon and 1 teaspoon, 3= uses measuring cups to measure a cup, 1/2 cup, 1/3 cup, 1/4 cup, 2= selects appropriate measuring cup for a cup, 1/2 cup, 1/3 cup, 1/4 cup, 1= when provided with the correct size measuring cup, fills the cup with liquid	

The AFLS® - Vocational Skills Protocol

The Assessment of Functional Living Skills - The AFLS®

Restaurant Kitchen (Continued)

TASK	SCORE	TASK NAME	TASK OBJECTIVE	QUESTION	EXAMPLE	CRITERIA	COMMENT
RK 6	0 1 2 3 4 0 1 2 3 4 0 1 2 3 4 0 1 2 3 4	Measures volumes	Learner will measure volumes of liquids and solids.	Can learner measure volumes of liquids and solids?	Cup, pint, quart, gallon (or metric equivalents), etc.	4= measures and states volumes in terms of cups, pints, quarts and gallons, 3= measures and states volumes in terms of at least 3 types of measures, 2= measures and states volumes in terms of at least 2 types of measures, 1= measures and states volumes in terms of at least 1 types of measure (cups, pints, quarts and gallons)	
RK 7	0 1 2 3 4 0 1 2 3 4 0 1 2 3 4 0 1 2 3 4	States abbreviations for standard measurements	Learner will state the measurement when shown their abbreviations.	Can learner identify abbreviations for standard measurements?	lbs, oz, in, ft, mi., yd., tsp., tbsp., C., pt., qt., gal, etc.	4= states the measurement unit for at least 10 abbreviations, 3= states the measurement unit for at least 6 abbreviations, 2= states the measurement unit for at least 4 abbreviations, 1= states the measurement unit for at least 2 abbreviations	
RK 8	0 1 2 3 4 0 1 2 3 4 0 1 2 3 4 0 1 2 3 4	Measures solid volume	Learner will measure solid volumes of a cup, 1/2 cup, 1/3 cup, 1/4 cup, 1 tablespoon, and 1 teaspoon.	Does learner measure the volume of solids?	Flour, sugar, etc.	4= measures solid volumes of a cup, 1/2, cup, 1/3 cup, 1/4 cup, 1 tablespoon and 1 teaspoon, 3= uses measuring cups to measure a cup, 1/2 cup, 1/3 cup, 1/4 cup, 2= selects appropriate measuring cup for a cup, 1/2 cup, 1/3 cup, 1/4 cup, 1= when provided with the correct size measuring cup, fills the cup with solids	
RK 9	0 1 2 3 4 0 1 2 3 4 0 1 2 3 4 0 1 2 3 4	States equivalent measures	Learner will state the equivalent units for at least 8 measures.	Can learner identify equivalent units of measures?	12 inches = foot, 36 inches in = yard, 3 feet = yard, 8 ounces = 1 cup, 16 ounces in a pint, 2 cups = pint, 2 pints = quart, 4 quarts = gallon, 16 ounces = a pound, etc.	4= states at least 8 equivalent measures including at least 1 from volume, length, and weight, 3= states at least 6 equivalent measures including at least 1 from volume, length, and weight, 2= states at least 4 equivalent measures, 1= states at least 2 equivalent measures	
RK 10	0 1 2 0 1 2 0 1 2 0 1 2	Uses can opener	Learner will use an electric or hand can opener to open cans without spilling contents.	Does learner use a can opener to open cans of food?		2= independently opens cans with electric or manual can opener with complete removal of the lid and without spilling, 1= opens cans with electric or manual can opener with only verbal prompts	NEEDS CLOSE SUPERVISION

Hygiene

TASK	SCORE	TASK NAME	TASK OBJECTIVE	QUESTION	EXAMPLE	CRITERIA	COMMENT
RK 11	0 1 2 0 1 2 0 1 2 0 1 2	Wears hair net or hat	Learner will wear hair net or hat when required.	Does learner wear a hair net or hat when required for work in a kitchen?		2= puts on and wears hair or hatnet as required, 1= requires assistance putting on hair net but will leave hair net or hat on as required	

The AFLS® - Vocational Skills Protocol

The Assessment of Functional Living Skills - The AFLS®

Restaurant Kitchen (Continued)

TASK	SCORE	TASK NAME	TASK OBJECTIVE	QUESTION	EXAMPLE	CRITERIA	COMMENT
RK 12	0 1 2 0 1 2 0 1 2 0 1 2	Wears apron	Learner will wear an apron when required for meal preparation.	Does learner wear an apron when required for meal preparation?		2= puts on and ties apron, 1= puts on apron but requires assistance tying	
RK 13	0 1 2 0 1 2 0 1 2 0 1 2	Washes hands as required	Learner will wash hands as required.	Does learner wash hands as required?		2= regularly washes hands after using restroom and prior to handling any kitchen appliances, dishes, utensils, or food materials, 1= washes hands appropriately after using restroom and when reminded in kitchen	
RK 14	0 1 2 0 1 2 0 1 2 0 1 2	Covers coughs to avoid spreading germs	Learner will cough into elbow or tissue.	Does learner cough into elbow or tissue?		2= coughs into elbow or tissue, 1= coughs into hands	
RK 15	0 1 2 3 4 0 1 2 3 4 0 1 2 3 4 0 1 2 3 4	Handles food in a hygienic manner	Learner will handle food in a hygienic manner.	Can learner handle food in a hygienic manner?		4= washes hands with hot water, uses gloves when handling poultry (if recommended by supervisor), keeps raw foods any equipment that has touched raw foods separated from those that have not touched raw foods, uses clean and sanitized work surface, sanitizes work surfaces when finished, 3= washes hands with hot water, uses gloves when handling poultry (if recommended by supervisor), keeps raw foods any equipment that has touched raw foods separated from those that have not touched raw foods, uses clean and sanitized work surface, 2= places food on clean surfaces and uses clean utensils, 1= washes hands prior to handling food	

Cooking

TASK	SCORE	TASK NAME	TASK OBJECTIVE	QUESTION	EXAMPLE	CRITERIA	COMMENT
RK 16	0 1 2 0 1 2 0 1 2 0 1 2	Makes salads	Learner will make salads.	Can learner make salads?		2= following store guidelines for size and ingredients, chops all necessary vegetables, places in plate or bowl, adds dressing, 1= chops all necessary ingredients according to store guidelines to be assembled later	
RK 17	0 1 2 0 1 2 0 1 2 0 1 2	Makes coffee	Learner will make coffee.	Can learner make coffee?		2= places filter, adds ground coffee, adds water, ensures pot is under spout, starts brew, 1= places filter, scoops coffee, adds water with verbal assistance	

The AFLS® - Vocational Skills Protocol

The Assessment of Functional Living Skills - The AFLS®

Restaurant Kitchen (Continued)

TASK	SCORE	TASK NAME	TASK OBJECTIVE	QUESTION	EXAMPLE	CRITERIA	COMMENT
RK 18	0 1 2 3 4 0 1 2 3 4 0 1 2 3 4 0 1 2 3 4	Completes a variety of food preparation activities	Learner will complete a variety of food preparation activities.	Can learner complete a variety of food preparations?	Makes hamburger patties, prepares deep fryer oil, preheats ovens, prepares lettuce leaves for sandwiches slices cucumbers for salads, makes toast, etc.	4= completes at least 10 food preparation activities, 3= completes at least 6 food preparation activities, 2= completes at least 4 food preparation activities, 1=completes at least 2 food preparation activities	
RK 19	0 1 2 3 4 0 1 2 3 4 0 1 2 3 4 0 1 2 3 4	Follows simple food items	Learner will prepare 10 simple food items.	Does learner prepare 10 simple food items?	Makes fruit salad, French fries, sandwiches, cole slaw, mashed potatoes, pancakes, hamburgers, etc.	4= follows recipe to independently prepare at least 10 simple food dishes, 3= prepares at least 6 dishes, 2= independently prepares at least 4 dishes, 1= follows recipe to prepare at least 2 simple dishes when provided with only verbal prompts	
RK 20	0 1 2 0 1 2 0 1 2 0 1 2	Places dishes into and out of oven	The learner will place dishes into and remove dishes from a hot oven.	Does learner put items into and remove them from a hot oven?		2= puts dishes into and removes dishes from a hot oven, 1= puts dishes into a hot oven	NEEDS CLOSE SUPERVISION
RK 21	0 1 2 0 1 2 0 1 2 0 1 2	Determines when food is fully cooked	Learner will determine when food is fully cooked.	Can learner determine when food is fully cooked?		2= identifies when food is finished cooking by reading thermometer, checking food by cutting into it, by observing color or texture chances, 1= identifies when food is finished cooking by reading thermometer or by requesting help from others to provide advice	NEEDS CLOSE SUPERVISION
RK 22	0 1 2 0 1 2 0 1 2 0 1 2	Serves appropriate portions on plates and bowls	Learner will serve appropriate portions on plates and bowls.	Can learner serve appropriate portions on plates and bowls?	When position requires scooping or placing food items onto a customer's plate	2= serves appropriate portions, 1= serves appropriate portions with only verbal prompts	
RK 23	0 1 2 0 1 2 0 1 2 0 1 2	Serves food on plates in a distributed and decorated manner	Learner will serve foods on plates in a distributed and decorated manner.	Can learner serve food on plates in a distributed and decorated manner?		2= arranges food on plates in distributed or decorative manner, 1= arranges food on plates with only verbal prompts	

The AFLS® - Vocational Skills Protocol

The Assessment of Functional Living Skills - The AFLS®

Warehouse

Identify products and preparing for shipping

TASK	SCORE	TASK NAME	TASK OBJECTIVE	QUESTION	EXAMPLE	CRITERIA	COMMENT
WH 1	0 1 2 0 1 2 0 1 2 0 1 2	Identifies content of boxes	Learner will identify contents of boxes.	Can learner identify contents of boxes?	Quantity, color, sizes, etc.	2= reads label or shipping documents and states the specific aspects of the items in the box or package (quantity, size, color, etc.), 1= identifies types of contents by written description on box (shirts, pants, etc.)	
WH 2	0 1 2 0 1 2 0 1 2 0 1 2	Locates inventory in warehouse	Learner will locate inventory in warehouse.	Can learner locate inventory in warehouse?		2= states location of items by row or location indicator (e.g, all the way in the back, E17, front row, etc.), and goes to physical location of items when given item name, SKU, model or part number, 1= goes to physical location of item given item name	
WH 3	0 1 2 0 1 2 0 1 2 0 1 2	Opens boxes	Learner will open boxes.	Can learner open boxes?	Uses a razor knife to open a box of shirts without cutting any of the shirts	2= safely uses box cutter or other sharp instrument to open boxes, 1= requires close supervision to safely open boxes with sharp instrument	NEEDS CLOSE SUPERVISION
WH 4	0 1 2 3 4 0 1 2 3 4 0 1 2 3 4 0 1 2 3 4	Picks items to be packed	Learner will pick items to be packed for shipping.	Can learner pick items to be packed for shipping?	Follows written list to pick 5 softballs, two catcher mitts, 1 can of chalk, and 3 Atlanta Braves hats.	4= follows written or verbal instructions to find and select up to 20 items from inventory, 3= follows written or verbal instructions to find and select up to 10 items from inventory, 2= finds and selects 5 items when told, 1= finds and selects 2 items when told	
WH 5	0 1 2 0 1 2 0 1 2 0 1 2	Packs items into boxes	When given items to be packaged for shipping, learner will select an appropriate size box, use packing materials to protect items, and seal the box.	Can learner pack items into boxes for shipping?		2= chooses appropriate size box, uses packing/ filler materials to protect contents, and seals box, 1= when given appropriate size box, uses packing/ filler materials to protect contents, and seals box with only verbal prompts	

The AFLS® - Vocational Skills Protocol

The Assessment of Functional Living Skills - The AFLS®

Warehouse (Continued)

TASK	SCORE	TASK NAME	TASK OBJECTIVE	QUESTION	EXAMPLE	CRITERIA	COMMENT
WH 6	0 1 2 3 4 0 1 2 3 4 0 1 2 3 4 0 1 2 3 4	Stacks boxes on pallets	Learner will stack boxes on pallets.	Can learner stack boxes on pallets?		4= stacks boxes (up to 50 lbs.) up to the height of learner's head in alternating pattern for each layer of boxes so boxes are stable and aligned, and applies wrapping material or bands to secure boxes together, 3= stacks boxes (up to 50 lbs.) in alternating pattern for each layer of boxes (so will not make single unsecured columns) so boxes are stable and aligned, 2= aligns boxes to fill a single layer on a pallet 1= aligns boxes to fill a single layer on a pallet when provided with only verbal prompts	NEEDS CLOSE SUPERVISION

Managing receipt of product inventory

TASK	SCORE	TASK NAME	TASK OBJECTIVE	QUESTION	EXAMPLE	CRITERIA	COMMENT
WH 7	0 1 2 3 4 0 1 2 3 4 0 1 2 3 4 0 1 2 3 4	Assembles boxes	Learner will assemble boxes.	Can learner assemble boxes?		4= assembles a box by taping the top and bottom or by interlocking top flaps to secure top without tape, 3= assembles a box by taping the top and bottom, 2= assembles and tapes bottom of a box, 1= assembles and tapes bottom of a box with verbal prompts	Consider moving this to warehouse skills or custodial?
WH 8	0 1 2 0 1 2 0 1 2 0 1 2	Breaks down boxes	Learner will break down boxes.	Can learner break down boxes?		2= cuts tape from boxes and folds flat, 1= requires close supervision to cut tape, independently folds boxes flat	NEEDS CLOSE SUPERVISION
WH 9	0 1 2 3 4 0 1 2 3 4 0 1 2 3 4 0 1 2 3 4	Verifies inventory received	Learner will verify that the paperwork matches the contents of goods received.	Can learner verify accuracy of contents of packages received?	Receives a shipment of 8 boxes with a list of items and confirms that all items on the list match contents of boxes	4= matches invoice or delivery bill of lading against items, uses item names, item SKUs, or abbreviations to determine whether receivables match paperwork in orders containing multiple boxes, 3= matches invoice or delivery bill of lading against items, uses item names, item SKUs, or abbreviations to determine whether receivables match paperwork for a single box, 2= matches invoice or delivery bill of lading against items names to determine whether receivables match paperwork, 1= when supervisor calls out item name and quantity, finds items and determines whether quantity matches what was called out	

The AFLS® - Vocational Skills Protocol

The Assessment of Functional Living Skills - The AFLS®

Warehouse (Continued)

TASK	SCORE	TASK NAME	TASK OBJECTIVE	QUESTION	EXAMPLE	CRITERIA	COMMENT
WH 10	0 1 2 0 1 2 0 1 2 0 1 2	Notes damaged or missing inventory	Learner will note damaged or missing to inventory.	Can learner note damaged or missing inventory?		2= when receiving a shipment of boxes, writes note on paperwork when items are missing or visibly damaged, 1= tells supervisor that items are missing or damaged	
WH 11	0 1 2 0 1 2 0 1 2 0 1 2	Manages inventory documents	Learner will manages inventory documents.	Can learner manage inventory documents?		2= saves paperwork or inventory documentation when it arrives in shipment, places in designated or appropriate location, 1= places paperwork in location directly told by supervisor at the time shipment arrives	

Moving products with machinery

TASK	SCORE	TASK NAME	TASK OBJECTIVE	QUESTION	EXAMPLE	CRITERIA	COMMENT
WS 12	0 1 2 0 1 2 0 1 2 0 1 2	Uses a manual pallet jack	Learner will use a manual pallet jack.	Can learner use a manual pallet jack?		2= places pallet jack under pallet, raises jack so pallet is not touching floor, moves pallet to designated location, lowers jack, removes jack from under pallet, 1= when provided with only verbal prompts, places pallet jack under pallet, raises jack so pallet is not touching floor, moves pallet to designated location, lowers jack, removes jack from under pallet	NEEDS CLOSE SUPERVISION
WS 13	0 1 2 0 1 2 0 1 2 0 1 2	Uses fork lift	Learner will use fork lift.	Can learner use forklift?	When a truck arrives, learner turns on, steers left and right, navigates around moving and stationary objects, loads pallet, retrieves palletized items from truck and drops in upper racks or shelving	2= operates fork lift safely, retrieves and places items to and from high locations such as upper racks or shelves, 1= operates fork lift safely, retrieves and places items on ground or bottom racks or shelves	NEEDS CLOSE SUPERVISION

The AFLS® - Vocational Skills Protocol

The Assessment of Functional Living Skills - The AFLS®

Tools

Hand tools

TASK	SCORE	TASK NAME	TASK OBJECTIVE	QUESTION	EXAMPLE	CRITERIA	COMMENT
TO 1	0 1 2 3 4 0 1 2 3 4 0 1 2 3 4 0 1 2 3 4	Hammers nails	Learner will hammer nails.	Can learner hammer nails?		4= aligns pieces to be nailed and nail two pieces of wood together, if nail is bent, removes nail without damaging material and hammers new one, removes nails with claw, 3= selects appropriate hammer and hammers nails of different sizes into different materials without bending nails or damaging materials, 2= hammers nails of different sizes into different materials including an 8d common nail, 5d finishing nail, and a brad, 1= when given appropriate hammer by supervisor, hammers 5d finishing nail where directed	NEEDS CLOSE SUPERVISION
TO 2	0 1 2 0 1 2 0 1 2 0 1 2	Uses advanced hammer skills	Learner will use a hammer and nails to attach boards together in various ways.	Can learner use a hammer and nails to attach boards together on the job?	Selects correct nail, aligns and hold boards, nails at angle, set a nail, realign if nail falls when setting, hammer overhead, avoids cracking or splitting boards, replacing boards that are damaged by nails, etc.	2= consistently demonstrates ability to perform with at least 6 advanced hammering skills, 1= consistently demonstrates ability to perform with at least 3 advanced hammering skills	NEEDS CLOSE SUPERVISION
TO 3	0 1 2 0 1 2 0 1 2 0 1 2	Identifies different types of nails	Learner will identify and select a variety of nails to be used for different tasks.	Can learner identify and select a variety of nails to be used for different tasks?	Finishing nails, brads, roofing nails, galvanized, common nails, box nails, spiral nails, etc., selects a short finishing nail to hand a light picture, uses a 3 inch common nail to connect 2X4s, uses finishing nails to attach baseboard molding, uses roofing nail to apply roofing shingles, etc.	2= identifies and selects at least 6 different types of nails for specific tasks, 1= identifies and selects at least 3 different types of nails for specific tasks	

The Assessment of Functional Living Skills - The AFLS®

Tools (Continued)

TASK	SCORE	TASK NAME	TASK OBJECTIVE	QUESTION	EXAMPLE	CRITERIA	COMMENT
TO 4	0 1 2 3 4 0 1 2 3 4 0 1 2 3 4 0 1 2 3 4	Uses screwdrivers	Learner will select the appropriate type and size of a screwdriver for a specific screw, and remove, insert, and tighten a screw.	Does learner identify the appropriate type and size of a screwdriver needed for a specific screw and use it to tighten and remove screws?	Identifies need for a small Philips head screwdriver, etc.	4= selects appropriate type and size of screwdriver, inserts screws into holes, and both tightens and removes screws, 3= selects appropriate type and size of screwdriver and both tightens a previously inserted screw, and removes a screw, 2= selects correct type and size of screwdriver, 1= selects correct type of screwdriver	
TO 5	0 1 2 0 1 2 0 1 2 0 1 2	Uses "advanced" screwdriver skills	Learner will use screwdriver and screws to secure or attach materials together.	Can learner use screwdriver and screws to secure or attaching materials together?	Attaching objects with pre-drilled holes, drills pilot hole, countersinking into drywall, removing screw with stripped head, correct size screwdriver, screwing in at an angle, etc.	2= consistently demonstrates ability to perform with at least 4 advanced screwdriver skills, 1= consistently demonstrates ability to perform with at least 2 advanced screwdriver skills	
TO 6	0 1 2 0 1 2 0 1 2 0 1 2	Selects screws for task	Learner will identify and select a variety of screws to be used for different tasks.	Can learner identify and select a variety of screw to be used for different tasks?	Wood screws, dry wall screws, sheet metal screws, round head screws, flat head screws, machine screws, slotted screws, etc.	2= identifies and selects at least 4 different types of screws for specific tasks, 1= identifies and selects at least 2 different types of screws for specific tasks	
TO 7	0 1 2 0 1 2 0 1 2 0 1 2	Uses hand saw	Learner will use a hand saw.	Can learner use a hand saw?	Hack saw, fine tooth saw, utility saw, coping saw, etc.	2= selects and uses correct hand saw to cut wood and metal items to designated length, 1= when given correct saw, cuts in straight line through a 2X4	NEEDS CLOSE SUPERVISION
TO 8	0 1 2 0 1 2 0 1 2 0 1 2	Uses sand paper to smooth rough wood	Learner will smooth rough wood with sand paper.	Does learner smooth rough wood with sand paper?		2= smooths various wooden objects with sand paper, 1= smooths wooden objects with sand paper with only verbal prompts	
TO 9	0 1 2 3 4 0 1 2 3 4 0 1 2 3 4 0 1 2 3 4	Uses pliers	Learner will use pliers.	Can learner use pliers?	Split joint, needle nose, long nose, short nose, locking pliers, channel lock, etc.	4= select correct pliers, uses pliers to hold, twist, bend, break, cut wires, and strip wires, 3= select correct pliers and tightly hold and bend items, 2= selecting correct pliers for task, 1= when given correct pliers, grabs and holds item with pliers	

The AFLS® - Vocational Skills Protocol

The Assessment of Functional Living Skills - The AFLS®

Tools (Continued)

TASK	SCORE	TASK NAME	TASK OBJECTIVE	QUESTION	EXAMPLE	CRITERIA	COMMENT
TO 10	0 1 2 0 1 2 0 1 2 0 1 2	Uses wrenches	Learner will use wrenches.	Can learner use wrenches?	Open ended, box wrench, combination, adjustable wrench, lug wrench, torque wrench, etc.	2= determines size and type of wrench to use, tightens and loosens bolts, 1= tightens or loosens bolts when given correct wrench	
TO 11	0 1 2 0 1 2 0 1 2 0 1 2	Uses socket wrenches	Learner will choose correct socket wrenches and socket to tighten or loosen bolts.	Can learner use socket wrenches?	Socket wrenches can be heavy duty or light weight, sockets can include: 1/8 inch, 1/4 inch, 1/2 inch, 3/4 inch, 8 mm, 10 mm, etc.	2= determines type of wrench and size of sockets to use to tighten and loosen bolts, 1= tightens or loosens bolts when given correct wrench and socket	
TO 12	0 1 2 0 1 2 0 1 2 0 1 2	Identifies and chooses correct nuts, bolts, and washers	Learner will identify and select a variety of nuts, bolts, and washers to be used for different tasks.	Can learner identify and select a variety of nuts, bolts, and washers to be used for different tasks?	Coarse or fine thread pattern, nut size, head shape- flat, domed, specific length, washers- locking, etc.	2= identifies and selects at least 4 different types of nuts, bolts, and washers for specific tasks, 1= identifies and selects at least 2 different types of nuts, bolts, and washers for specific tasks	
TO 13	0 1 2 3 4 0 1 2 3 4 0 1 2 3 4 0 1 2 3 4	Uses measuring tape	Learner will measure with a measuring tape.	Can learner measure with a measuring tape?		4= measures up to 50 feet to nearest 1/8 inch, 3= measures up to 25 feet to the nearest 1/4 inch, 2= measures with tape measure to 1/2 inch, 1= measures with tape measure to nearest inch	
TO 14	0 1 2 0 1 2 0 1 2 0 1 2	Strikes chalk lines	Learner will strike chalk lines.	Can learner strike chalk lines?		2= measures distance from other objects in two places and "snaps" chalk line in between those marks, 1= "snaps" chalk line between to points marked by others	
TO 15	0 1 2 0 1 2 0 1 2 0 1 2	Uses a stud finder	Learner will use a stud finder to locate boards located behind walls.	Can the learner use a stud finder?	Locates 2x4 behind finished wall	2= locates studs behind walls using a stud finder, 1= locates studs behind walls using a stud finder with only verbal prompts	
TO 16	0 1 2 0 1 2 0 1 2 0 1 2	Uses a level	Learner will use a level to check for accurate horizontal and vertical placement of items.	Can the learner use a level to check for accurate horizontal and vertical placement of items?	Ensures a picture is hanging correctly, etc.	2= uses a level to check for accurate horizontal and vertical placement of items, 1= uses a level to check for accurate horizontal and vertical placement of items with only verbal prompts	

The AFLS® - Vocational Skills Protocol

The Assessment of Functional Living Skills - The AFLS®

Tools (Continued)

TASK	SCORE	TASK NAME	TASK OBJECTIVE	QUESTION	EXAMPLE	CRITERIA	COMMENT
TO 17	0 1 2 0 1 2 0 1 2 0 1 2	Uses a caulking gun	Learner will use caulk gun.	Can learner use caulk gun?		2= neatly applies caulk to corners and straight lines, 1= neatly applies caulk to straight lines	
TO 18	0 1 2 0 1 2 0 1 2 0 1 2	Uses two tools at the same time to accomplish task	Learner will use 2 tools at the same time once to accomplish tasks.	Can learner use 2 tools at the same time to accomplish task?	Uses a wrench to hold a nut and another to tighten bolt, uses pliers to hold nut while using screwdriver to tighten screw, etc.	2= uses 2 tools at the same time to accomplish task, 1= uses 2 tools at the same time to accomplish task with only verbal prompts	

Power tools

TASK	SCORE	TASK NAME	TASK OBJECTIVE	QUESTION	EXAMPLE	CRITERIA	COMMENT
TO 19	0 1 2 0 1 2 0 1 2 0 1 2	Uses a nail gun	Learner will use a nail gun to attach boards and other materials.	Can learner use a nail gun?	Framing, roofing, decking, etc.	2= safely operates nail gun including loading the gun, nailing, and storing when finished, 1= safely nails objects when nail gun is loaded by supervisor	NEEDS CLOSE SUPERVISION
TO 20	0 1 2 0 1 2 0 1 2 0 1 2	Operates a sander	Learner will use a sander.	Can learner use a sander?	Belt or orbital sander, etc.	2= chooses correct sandpaper, replaces sand paper when worn, 1= uses sand paper to smooth wooden surfaces	NEEDS CLOSE SUPERVISION
TO 21	0 1 2 3 4 0 1 2 3 4 0 1 2 3 4 0 1 2 3 4	Sands wood	Learner will smooth wood surfaces by using both orbital and belt sanders, choosing appropriate grade of sand paper, and switching to finer grades as needed.	Can learner use orbital and belt sanders to smooth wood?	Remove materials, make wood smooth, with the grain, overlapping strokes, even application of force, etc.	4= chooses appropriate grade of sand paper, switches to finer grades as needed, uses both orbital and belt sanders, 3= chooses appropriate grade of sand paper, switches to finer grades as needed, uses orbital or belt sander, 2= when given appropriate sand paper on sander, sands level surfaces stopping when smooth, 1= when given appropriate sand paper on sander, requires only verbal prompts to sand	NEEDS CLOSE SUPERVISION
TO 22	0 1 2 3 4 0 1 2 3 4 0 1 2 3 4 0 1 2 3 4	Uses electric saws	Learner will use electric saws.	Can learner use electric saws?	Circular saw, jig saw, table saw, tile saw, sawsall, drywall saw, etc.	4= safely uses at least 4 kinds of saws, 3= safely uses 2 kinds of saws, 2= safely uses a saw, 1= requires close supervision and verbal prompts to saw	NEEDS CLOSE SUPERVISION

The Assessment of Functional Living Skills - The AFLS®

Tools (Continued)

TASK	SCORE	TASK NAME	TASK OBJECTIVE	QUESTION	EXAMPLE	CRITERIA	COMMENT
TO 23	0 1 2 0 1 2 0 1 2 0 1 2	Cuts with saw	Learner will cut with saws using advanced techniques.	Can learner cut at specified angles and depths, and rip boards lengthwise?		2= cuts on line at specified angles and depth, and rips boards lengthwise, 1= requires verbal prompts to cut on line at specified angles and depths, and to rip boards lengthwise	NEEDS CLOSE SUPERVISION
TO 24	0 1 2 0 1 2 0 1 2 0 1 2	Selects saw blades for task	Learner will choose appropriate blades required for cutting tasks.	Can learner choose appropriate blades required for cutting tasks?	Plywood blade, ripping blade, etc.	2= selects appropriate blade for cutting task, changes blades as needed, 1= changes blades with verbal prompts	NEEDS CLOSE SUPERVISION
TO 25	0 1 2 3 4 0 1 2 3 4 0 1 2 3 4 0 1 2 3 4	Uses drills	Learner will use drills.	Can learner use drills?		4= selects and changes drill bits, drills holes, screws and unscrews, 3= drills holes and changes drill bits, 2= marks starting point, makes pilot hole, drills hole, switches bit direction, 1= given an installed bit and a pilot hole in surface, drills hole	NEEDS CLOSE SUPERVISION
TO 26	0 1 2 3 4 0 1 2 3 4 0 1 2 3 4 0 1 2 3 4	Builds small structures combining several tools	Learner will use multiple tools to build small structures or objects.	Can learner use multiple tools to build small structures or objects?	Uses tape measure, chalk line, saw, hammer and nails, builder's square, and level etc. to construct a wall frame, constructs soffit to cover HVAC ductwork, builds a toy box, or small step stool for child's bathroom, builds a planter for outside plants, etc.	4= plans and builds small structures or objects using 3 or more tools, 3= plans a small building project with verbal assistance to use at least 3 different tools to build a structure or object, 2= follows a model or written instructions to use at least 3 different tools to build a structure or object, 1= uses at least 3 different tools to build a structure or object with only verbal prompts	NEEDS CLOSE SUPERVISION
TO 27	0 1 2 0 1 2 0 1 2 0 1 2	Cares for tools and equipment	Learner will maintain tools and equipment.	Can learner maintain of tools and equipment?	Dusts shavings off of saw and places back in storage case, puts sockets back in tool box after use to avoid misplacing them, etc.	2= keeps tools in organized location, puts tools back into location when finished using them, cleans and cares for tools as needed, 1= puts tools into location when told to do so by others	
TO 28	0 1 2 0 1 2 0 1 2 0 1 2	Cares for tools and equipment during use	Learner will keep track of tools and equipment when not being used for short period of time.	Can learner keep track of tools and equipment when not being used for short period of time?	Places hammer in tool belt when not hammering, consistently places tools level, tape measure, and chalk line in same bucket every day, etc.	2= while working on projects, consistently places tools in certain location when finished so as to be easy to find when needed next, 1= puts tools into same location with only verbal prompts	

The AFLS® - Vocational Skills Protocol

The Assessment of Functional Living Skills - The AFLS®

Tools (Continued)

Tool knowledge

TASK	SCORE	TASK NAME	TASK OBJECTIVE	QUESTION	EXAMPLE	CRITERIA	COMMENT
TO 29	0 1 2 3 4 0 1 2 3 4 0 1 2 3 4 0 1 2 3 4	States the name of job-related tools and equipment given its function	Learner will identify job-related tools and equipment required for numerous tasks.	Can learner identify job-related tools and equipment required for numerous tasks?	What do you use to hammer a nail? Learner says, "hammer." What do you tighten nuts with? Learner says, "A wrench."	4= identifies 10 job-related tools and equipment, 3= 8 job-related tools and equipment, 2= 4 job-related tools and equipment, 1= 2 job-related tools and equipment	
TO 30	0 1 2 3 4 0 1 2 3 4 0 1 2 3 4 0 1 2 3 4	States functions of job-related tools and equipment	Learner will identify the function of job-related tools and equipment.	Can learner identify the function of job-related tools and equipment?	What do you use a hammer for? Learner says, to drive nails. What do you use a wrench for? Learner says, "To tighten nuts and bolts."	4= identifies the function of 10 job-related tools and equipment, 3= function of 8 job-related tools and equipment, 2= function of 4 job-related tools and equipment, 1= function of 2 job-related tools and equipment	

The AFLS® - Vocational Skills Protocol

The Assessment of Functional Living Skills - The AFLS®

Trades and Construction

General construction

TASK	SCORE	TASK NAME	TASK OBJECTIVE	QUESTION	EXAMPLE	CRITERIA	COMMENT
TC 1	0 1 2 0 1 2 0 1 2 0 1 2	Delivers items to people on job site	Learner will deliver items to people on job site.	Can learner deliver items to people on job site?	Take this electrical outlet downstairs and give it to the electrician, bring the nail gun over to building 13 and give it to Tommy, go to the new excavation site and give these papers to the new foreman, etc.	2= delivers items of various sizes to familiar and unfamiliar people and to familiar and unfamiliar locations on a job site, 1= delivers small items to familiar people in familiar locations	
TC 2	0 1 2 0 1 2 0 1 2 0 1 2	Moves items on construction site	Learner will move equipment or materials on job site.	Can learner move equipment and materials on job site?	Brings stack of plywood to basement of home being careful not to bring so much that stack of wood interferes with laying the new floor, moves drywall from first floor to third floor and delivers to rooms so dry walls installers have a ready supply, carries roofing shingles from driveway to roof and stacks so roofers can quickly access the shingles, etc.	2= makes determinations about how to arrange delivered materials, quantities needed in certain areas, and evaluates when additional materials are needed to complete the task, 1= moves materials when provided with specific instructions and careful supervision	

Painting

TASK	SCORE	TASK NAME	TASK OBJECTIVE	QUESTION	EXAMPLE	CRITERIA	COMMENT
TC 3	0 1 2 0 1 2 0 1 2 0 1 2	Removes and replaces electrical outlet covers	Learner will remove and replace electrical plate covers.	Does learner remove and replace electrical plate covers?		2= removes and replaces electrical plate covers, 1= removes and replaces electrical plate coverswith only verbal prompts	
TC 4	0 1 2 0 1 2 0 1 2 0 1 2	Tapes edges	Learner will apply masking tape to edges of areas not to be painted.	Can learner apply masking tape to edges of areas not to be painted?	Apples masking tape to sides of door frame, around windows, and on trim to prevent paint contact	2= tapes around the edges of windows, outlets, doors, and the edges of walls or ceiling to prevent paint from contacting the taped areas, 1= independently tapes around straight edges, requires verbal prompts to tape around corners or curved areas	
TC 5	0 1 2 0 1 2 0 1 2 0 1 2	Uses drop cloths	Learner will use drop cloths to prevent paint from contacting the floor and furniture.	Can learner put down drop cloths to prevent paint from contacting the floor and furniture?	Places drop cloth on floor or over objects to prevent splashes and spills from contacting covered items	2= spreads and arranges drop clothes that prevent dripping or over spraying from contacting floor and furniture, 1= secures drop clothes to floor but needs verbal prompts to ensure other areas of objects are covered	

The AFLS® - Vocational Skills Protocol

The Assessment of Functional Living Skills - The AFLS®

Trades and Construction (Continued)

TASK	SCORE	TASK NAME	TASK OBJECTIVE	QUESTION	EXAMPLE	CRITERIA	COMMENT
TC 6	0 1 2 0 1 2 0 1 2 0 1 2	Prepares to paint	Learner will prepare paint prior to painting.	Can learner prepare paint prior to painting?	Dips brush into paint can so only tip of brush contains paint, rubs end of brush against inside lid of paint can to remove excess paint, orients brush downward to prevent paint from dripping back to handle, etc.	2= thoroughly shakes or stirs paint can, pries opens lid, pours into smaller container or roller tray, pours excess back into can when painting is finished, seals lid, wipes can clean, 1= thoroughly stirs paint	
TC 7	0 1 2 0 1 2 0 1 2 0 1 2	Paints with brush	Learner will paint with brush.	Can learner paint with brush?	Dips brush into paint can so only tip of brush contains paint, rubs end of brush against inside lid of paint can to remove excess paint, orients brush downward to prevent paint from dripping back to handle, etc.	2= paints trim around windows and doors, around and behind outlet covers, corners with paint brush ensuring the paint does not drip or run into areas not designated for paint, 1= paints trim around windows and doors, around and behind outlet covers, corners with paint brush, requires verbal prompts to prevent dripping	
TC 8	0 1 2 0 1 2 0 1 2 0 1 2	Paints with rollers	Learner will paint with rollers.	Can learner paint with rollers?	After wall around the edges of windows have been taped and painted, rolls paint on evenly, using overlapping rolls, multiple coats, and using a ladder or roller extension to reach areas near ceiling	2= when trim work has been finished, paints and fully covers an approximately 10 X 10 ft (3.5 X 3.5 M) area of a wall with roller ensuring the paint on edges does not run into areas not designated for paint, 1= paints with roller but requires verbal prompts to ensure full paint coverage on wall surfaces	
TC 9	0 1 2 0 1 2 0 1 2 0 1 2	Cleans brushes and rollers	Learner will clean brushes and rollers.	Can learner clean brushes and rollers?	Uses paint thinner to clean oil based paints from brushes, rollers, roller tray, roller handle, uses water to clean latex paint from brushes, rollers, roller tray, roller handle, etc.	2= cleans water-based and oil-based paint from rollers and brushes, 1= cleans water-based paint from rollers and brushes	NEEDS CLOSE SUPERVISION

Plumbing

TASK	SCORE	TASK NAME	TASK OBJECTIVE	QUESTION	EXAMPLE	CRITERIA	COMMENT
TC 10	0 1 2 3 4 0 1 2 3 4 0 1 2 3 4 0 1 2 3 4	Cuts PVC, ABS, and copper pipes	Learner will cut PVC, ABS, and copper pipes.	Can learner cut PVC, ABS, and copper pipes?	Measures and marks 12 inches on a copper pipe, fits and cuts with copper pipe cutter, uses hack saw to cut off an 8 inch section of ABS pipe	4= cuts copper, ABS, and PVC pipes to specified lengths, 3= cuts ABS and PVC pipes to specified lengths, 2= cuts ABS and PVC pipes where marked by supervisor, 1= cuts ABS or PVC pipes where marked by supervisor with only verbal prompts	NEEDS CLOSE SUPERVISION

The Assessment of Functional Living Skills - The AFLS®

Trades and Construction (Continued)

TASK	SCORE	TASK NAME	TASK OBJECTIVE	QUESTION	EXAMPLE	CRITERIA	COMMENT
TC 11	0 1 2 3 4 0 1 2 3 4 0 1 2 3 4 0 1 2 3 4	Assembles pipes	Learner will assemble pipes.	Can learner assemble pipes?	Assembles and glues pipes for in-ground sprinkler system with pipes pointed upwards for sprinkler head mounts	4= connects multiple pipes and fittings, oriented in correct directions, 3= connects multiple pipes and fittings, oriented in correct directions, with only verbal prompts, 2= glues ABS or PVC pipes to a single fitting, 1= glues ABS or PVC pipes to a single fitting with only verbal prompts	
TC 12	0 1 2 0 1 2 0 1 2 0 1 2	Installs or replaces hose bib (spigot)	Learner will replace a hose bib.	Can learner replace a hose bib?	Shuts off water to house, opens spigot valve to drain water, uses wrench to remove hose bib, wraps Teflon tape around male threads, screws on hose bib, tightens with wrench, turns on water supply to house	2= removes old hose bib and installs new one, 1= removes and installs new hose bib with verbal prompts	
TC 13	0 1 2 0 1 2 0 1 2 0 1 2	Removes and replaces a P-trap	Learner will remove and replace a sink P-trap.	Can learner replace a sink P-trap?	Places a bucket under P-trap, unscrews connectors, removes and drains P-trap, cleans or replaces with a new P-trap, tightens connectors, turns on water and checks for leaks	2= removes old P-trap, installs new or cleaned P trap, 1= removes old P-trap, installs new or cleaned P-trap with only verbal prompts	
TC 14	0 1 2 0 1 2 0 1 2 0 1 2	Installs or replaces faucet	Learner will replace a faucet.	Can learner replace a faucet?	Shuts off water to faucet, removes faucet, installs new faucet, attaches water pipes, turns on water to faucet	2= removes old faucet and installs new one, 1= removes and installs new faucet with verbal prompts	
TC 15	0 1 2 0 1 2 0 1 2 0 1 2	Makes minor toilet repairs	Learner will make minor toilet repairs.	Can learner make minor toilet repairs?	Stop leak by adjusting over flow control, caulk around toilet base, replace toilet handles, tightens screws on seat, replaces plunger chain, replaces flapper or stopper, changes toilet seat, etc.	2= repairs 4 common toilet problems, 1= repairs 2 common toilet problems	

The AFLS® - Vocational Skills Protocol

The Assessment of Functional Living Skills - The AFLS®

Trades and Construction (Continued)

Wiring & electrical

TASK	SCORE	TASK NAME	TASK OBJECTIVE	QUESTION	EXAMPLE	CRITERIA	COMMENT
TC 16	0 1 2 0 1 2 0 1 2 0 1 2	Turns off main electricity	Learner will turn off entire house or unit or individual circuits.	Can learner turn off entire house or unit or individual circuits?	Finds circuit breaker, turns off circuit to kitchen of house so new electrical outlet can be installed	2= turns on and off power to specified circuits, 1= turns on and off power to entire house or unit	NEEDS CLOSE SUPERVISION
TC 17	0 1 2 3 4 0 1 2 3 4 0 1 2 3 4 0 1 2 3 4	Resets a circuit breaker	Learner will reset a circuit breaker and reset a GFIC button.	Can learner reset a circuit breaker and reset a GFIC button?		4= locates and resets tripped (flipped switch) circuit breaker, resets circuit, 3= finds circuit breaker box independently, but requires verbal prompts to locate correct circuit and resets independently, 2= locates and resets GFIC button on outlets, 1= locates and resets GFIC button on outlet with only verbal prompts	Warning: Learner must not be allowed to open a circuit breaker panel until fully understands the danger of electricity and how to avoid being shocked
TC 18	0 1 2 0 1 2 0 1 2 0 1 2	Twists wires together	Learner will twist different types of wires together.	Can learner twist multi-strand and solid copper wires together?		2= twists solid copper and multi-strand wires together by hand or by using wire twisting tool tightly and neatly for solid connection, 1= twists lightweight, multi-strand, wires together by hand	
TC 19	0 1 2 3 4 0 1 2 3 4 0 1 2 3 4 0 1 2 3 4	Strips and connects wires	Learner will strip and connect wires.	Can learner strip and connect wires?		4= uses wire cutters to strip the insulation from wires of various gauges, connects wires with connector caps, 3= uses wire cutters to strip the insulation from wires of various gauges, with only verbal prompts, independently uses wire connectors to connect wires, 2= connects stripped wires together using wire connector caps, 1= connects stripped wires together using wire connector caps with only verbal prompts	NEEDS CLOSE SUPERVISION
TC 20	0 1 2 0 1 2 0 1 2 0 1 2	Attaches wires to electrical outlets or switches	Learner will attach wires to electrical outlets or switches.	Can learner attach wires to electrical outlets or switches?		2= attaches wires to electrical outlet or switches in outlet box, 1= attaches wires to electrical outlet or switches in outlet box with only verbal prompts	NEEDS CLOSE SUPERVISION

The Assessment of Functional Living Skills - The AFLS®

Trades and Construction (Continued)

TASK	SCORE	TASK NAME	TASK OBJECTIVE	QUESTION	EXAMPLE	CRITERIA	COMMENT
TC 21	0 1 2 0 1 2 0 1 2 0 1 2	Tests for electrical current	Learner will test for electrical current or "live" wires.	Can learner test for electrical current or "live" wires?	Holds voltage detector near wires to determine whether there is a live current	2= uses electrical voltage detector to determine whether wires contain electrical current, 1= uses electrical voltage detector to determine whether wires contain electrical current with only verbal prompts	NEEDS CLOSE SUPERVISION
TC 22	0 1 2 0 1 2 0 1 2 0 1 2	Identifies and selects wires for specified task	Learner will identify and select a variety of wires and cables to be used for different tasks.	Can learner identify and select a variety of wires and cables to be used for different tasks?	Solid core wires, braided wires, lamp cord, grounded or ungrounded wires of varying gauges, HDMI, optical cable, component cable, Ethernet cables, telephone line, coaxial, etc.	2= identifies and selects at least 6 different types of wires and cables for specific tasks, 1= identifies and selects at least 3 different types of wires and cables for specific tasks	
TC 23	0 1 2 0 1 2 0 1 2 0 1 2	Attaches computer wiring	Learner will attach computer wiring.	Can learner attach computer wiring?	2= connects mouse, hard drive (CPU), monitor, etc. to one another in appropriate configuration, 1= requires only verbal prompts to attach computer wires and cables		

Drywall

TASK	SCORE	TASK NAME	TASK OBJECTIVE	QUESTION	EXAMPLE	CRITERIA	COMMENT
TC 24	0 1 2 0 1 2 0 1 2 0 1 2	Cuts drywall	Learner will cut drywall to specified dimensions.	Can learner cut drywall to specified dimensions?		2= measures and cuts drywall to specified dimensions, 1= neatly cuts drywall when drywall is premeasured and marked for cutting	NEEDS CLOSE SUPERVISION
TC 25	0 1 2 3 4 0 1 2 3 4 0 1 2 3 4 0 1 2 3 4	Installs drywall	Learner will install drywall.	Can learner install drywall?	Measuring pieces, cutting to size, applying glue, screwing into frame or studs, taping, "mudding," etc.	4= attaches dry wall to all surfaces including ceiling, 3= attaches full, and cuts and attaches partial sheets of drywall to wall frame, 2= attaches full (4 X 8 ft.) sheets of drywall to wall frame, 1= assists supervisor by holding panels in place	
TC 26	0 1 2 3 4 0 1 2 3 4 0 1 2 3 4 0 1 2 3 4	Tapes dry wall	Learner will apply drywall tape to seams between sheets of drywall.	Can learner apply drywall tape to seams between sheets of drywall?		4= tapes edges of doors and windows, vertical corners of rooms, vertical edges of ceiling, 3= tapes edges of doors and windows, vertical corners of rooms, vertical edges of ceiling with only verbal prompts, 2= tapes flat straight edges of sheets of drywall in middle of wall, 1= tapes flat straight edges of sheets of drywall in middle of wall with only verbal prompts	

The AFLS® - Vocational Skills Protocol

The Assessment of Functional Living Skills - The AFLS®

Trades and Construction (Continued)

TASK	SCORE	TASK NAME	TASK OBJECTIVE	QUESTION	EXAMPLE	CRITERIA	COMMENT
TC 27	0 1 2 3 4 0 1 2 3 4 0 1 2 3 4 0 1 2 3 4	Muds and sands drywall	Learner will apply and sand drywall joint compound "mud."	Can learner apply and sand drywall joint compound?		4= applies layer of mud to all seams, corners, and edges of uneven surfaces of drywall and sands walls smooth, 3= applies layer of mud to all seams, corners, and edges of uneven surfaces of drywall with only verbal prompts, 2= independently applies layer of mud to seams on flat surfaces of drywall, requires verbal prompts to sand wall smooth, 1= applies layer of mud to seams on flat surfaces of drywall	

Roofing

TASK	SCORE	TASK NAME	TASK OBJECTIVE	QUESTION	EXAMPLE	CRITERIA	COMMENT
TC 28	0 1 2 3 4 0 1 2 3 4 0 1 2 3 4 0 1 2 3 4	Remains safe on roof	Learner will install new roof.	Can learner install new roof?	Uses safety line, safety harness guard rails, approach edges cautiously, wears shoes or boots with adequate traction, ensures no loose tools or objects are left on roof, cautious while getting onto or off of ladder, to install satellite dish, repair leaky roof, clean gutters of house, etc.	4= safely completes job-related activities while on roof, 3= safely carries objects on roof, 2= safely maneuvers on roof without supervision, 1= safely climbs on and off roof from ladder	NEEDS CLOSE SUPERVISION
TC 29	0 1 2 0 1 2 0 1 2 0 1 2	Removes existing roof	Learner will remove existing roof.	Can learner remove an existing roof?	Tears out old shingles, removes old roofing felt and nails, throws to ground safely ensuring no one is below, etc.	2= safely removes existing roof, 1= safely removes existing roof with only verbal prompts	NEEDS CLOSE SUPERVISION
TC 30	0 1 2 0 1 2 0 1 2 0 1 2	Lays felt roofing paper	Learner will install roof felt to roof.	Can learner install roof felt to roof?		2= strikes chalk lines, rolls felt onto roof along chalk line, cuts roll to size, nails to roof, 1= nails roofing felt to roof	NEEDS CLOSE SUPERVISION
TC 31	0 1 2 3 4 0 1 2 3 4 0 1 2 3 4 0 1 2 3 4	Installs roofing shingles	Leaner will install roofing shingles.	Can learner install roofing shingles?		4= snaps chalk line, installs shingles in staggered overlapping pattern on line, nails shingles, cuts excess shingle from end of roof line, 3= nails shingles, cuts excess shingle from end of roof line, 2= when row of shingles is started by supervisor, lays and nails next shingles in row, 1= nails shingles laid by supervisor	NEEDS CLOSE SUPERVISION

The AFLS® - Vocational Skills Protocol

The Assessment of Functional Living Skills - The AFLS®

Trades and Construction (Continued)

Carpeting

TASK	SCORE	TASK NAME	TASK OBJECTIVE	QUESTION	EXAMPLE	CRITERIA	COMMENT
TC 32	0 1 2 0 1 2 0 1 2 0 1 2	Cuts carpet and padding	Learner will cut carpet and padding to specified dimensions.	Can learner cut carpet and padding to specified dimensions?		2= measures and cuts carpet and carpet padding to specified dimensions, 1= neatly cuts carpet and padding when premeasured and marked for cutting	NEEDS CLOSE SUPERVISION
TC 33	0 1 2 0 1 2 0 1 2 0 1 2	Applies tack strips	Learner will apply carpet tack strips to edges of room.	Can learner apply carpet tack strips to edges of room?		2= cuts and nails carpet tack strips to edges of room, 1= cuts and nails carpet tack strips to edges of room with only verbal prompts	
TC 34	0 1 2 0 1 2 0 1 2 0 1 2	Staples carpet padding to subfloor	Learner will staple carpet padding to subfloor.	Can learner staple carpet padding to subfloor?		2= rolls out carpet padding, positions padding evenly throughout room, attaches to floor, 1= attaches to floor where directed by supervisor	
TC 35	0 1 2 0 1 2 0 1 2 0 1 2	Lays carpet	Learner will lay carpet.	Can learner lay carpet?		2= measures carpet, cuts straight lines, rolls carpet on floor, 1= measures carpet, cuts straight lines, rolls carpet on floor with only verbal prompts	
TC 36	0 1 2 0 1 2 0 1 2 0 1 2	Stretches carpet to tack strips	Learner will use a stretching tool to stretch carpet and affix to carpet tack strips.	Can learner use a stretching tool to stretch carpet and affix to carpet tack strips?		2= uses carpet stretcher to affix carpet to tack strips, 1= uses carpet stretcher to affix carpet to tack strips with only verbal prompts	

Automotive

TASK	SCORE	TASK NAME	TASK OBJECTIVE	QUESTION	EXAMPLE	CRITERIA	COMMENT
TC 37	0 1 2 0 1 2 0 1 2 0 1 2	Checks and adjusts tire pressure	Learner will check and adjust tire pressure.	Can learner check and adjust tire pressure?		2= uses tire pressure gauge to determine air pressure, adds or lets out air to reach a specified amount of pressure, 1= reads tire pressure gauge	NEEDS CLOSE SUPERVISION
TC 38	0 1 2 3 4 0 1 2 3 4 0 1 2 3 4 0 1 2 3 4	Rotates and changes tires	Learner will remove, replace, and rotate tires and wheels.	Can learner remove, replace, rotate tires and wheels?		4= uses machine to remove and replace tire on wheel, 3= rotates wheels and tires back to front or side to side, 2= removes and replaces wheel and tire, 1= removes and replaces wheel and tire with verbal prompts	NEEDS CLOSE SUPERVISION

The AFLS® - Vocational Skills Protocol

The Assessment of Functional Living Skills - The AFLS®

Trades and Construction (Continued)

TASK	SCORE	TASK NAME	TASK OBJECTIVE	QUESTION	EXAMPLE	CRITERIA	COMMENT
TC 39	0 1 2 0 1 2 0 1 2 0 1 2	Performs routine automotive cleaning tasks	Learner will perform a variety of routine automotive cleaning tasks.	Can learner perform a variety of routine automotive cleaning tasks?	Vacuums interior carpets, vacuums floor mats, dusts dashboard, washes windows, washes exterior of car, waxes, cleans wheels, applies tire shine, etc.	2= performs 5 routine automotive cleaning tasks, 1= performs 3 routine automotive cleaning tasks	NEEDS CLOSE SUPERVISION
TC 40	0 1 2 0 1 2 0 1 2 0 1 2	Performs routine automotive maintenance tasks	Learner will perform a variety of routine automotive maintenance tasks.	Can learner perform a variety of routine automotive maintenance tasks?	Checks oil, adds oil to vehicle, changes oil filter, changes air filter, replaces windshield wipers, checks windshield wiper fluid, tops off fluids, pumps gas, etc.	2= performs 5 routine automotive maintenance tasks, 1= performs 3 routine automotive maintenance tasks	NEEDS CLOSE SUPERVISION

The AFLS® - Vocational Skills Protocol

The Assessment of Functional Living Skills - The AFLS®

Landscaping
Plant maintenance

TASK	SCORE	TASK NAME	TASK OBJECTIVE	QUESTION	EXAMPLE	CRITERIA	COMMENT
LN 1	0 1 2 0 1 2 0 1 2 0 1 2	Uses hoses	Learner will use hoses.	Can learner use hoses?		2= attaches and removes hoses from spigot, connects hose attachments, controls kinks when using hose, coils hose after use, 1= uncoils and pulls hose to desired location, turns spigot on and off	
LN 2	0 1 2 3 4 0 1 2 3 4 0 1 2 3 4 0 1 2 3 4	Waters plants	Learner will water plants.	Can learner water plants?	Waters plants with using thumb or sprayer to create desired stream pattern	4= independently identifies plants in need of watering and applies an adequate amount of water to plants using an appropriate spray pattern, 3= waters specified plants including independently adjusts water flow patterns, 2= waters specified plants when provided with only verbal prompts and when water flow patterns are adjusted for learner, 1= waters specified plants when provided with only verbal prompts and water flow patterns are adjusted for learner	
LN 3	0 1 2 3 4 0 1 2 3 4 0 1 2 3 4 0 1 2 3 4	Plants plants	Learner will plant plants.	Can learner plant plants?	Plants a dozen pansies	4= digs hole with a trowel/hand shovel, plants a plant at a correct depth, fills in dirt, compresses soil around plant, 3= adjusts soil so plant will be inserted to a correct depth in an existing hole and inserts, fills in, and compresses soil around plant, 2= removes pot, and places plant in an existing hole, fills in dirt, and compresses soil around plant, 1= removes pot, and places plant in an existing hole, fills in dirt, and compresses soil around plant when provided with only verbal prompts	

Plant maintenance

TASK	SCORE	TASK NAME	TASK OBJECTIVE	QUESTION	EXAMPLE	CRITERIA	COMMENT
LN 4	0 1 2 0 1 2 0 1 2 0 1 2	Removes dead plants and yard waste	Learner will remove dead plants and yard waste.	Can learner remove dead plants and yard waste?	Pulled weeds, sticks, pruned shrubs, leaves and debris from trimmed hedges, etc.	2= after pruning, weeding, or other gardening or yard tasks have concluded, makes piles and removes all dead plants or yard waste to yard bags or approved trash receptacle, 1= places yard waste into bags or trash receptacle after put in to piles by supervisor or coworker	

The AFLS® - Vocational Skills Protocol

Landscaping (Continued)

TASK	SCORE	TASK NAME	TASK OBJECTIVE	QUESTION	EXAMPLE	CRITERIA	COMMENT
LN 5	0 1 2 0 1 2 0 1 2 0 1 2	Applies mulch	Learner will apply and spread mulch.	Can learner apply mulch?		2= estimates number of bags of mulch needed to cover designated area, stacks bags near area, and spreads mulch evenly in area, 1= once bags of mulch have been dumped out, spreads evenly throughout bed	

Use of garden hand tools

COMMENT

TASK	SCORE	TASK NAME	TASK OBJECTIVE	QUESTION	EXAMPLE	CRITERIA	COMMENT
LN 6	0 1 2 3 4 0 1 2 3 4 0 1 2 3 4 0 1 2 3 4	Uses shovels	Learner will use a shovel to dig.	Can learner dig with a shovel?	Digs a trench for sprinkler pipe, digs hole to plant flower, etc.	4= removes and sets aside sod, digs holes and trenches to a depth of at least 12 inches for 6-8 feet, 3= digs a hole at least 12 inches in diameter to a depth of at least 12 inches, 2= digs an 8 inch diameter hole with a shovel to a depth of at least 8 inches in diameter when provided with only verbal prompts, 1= shovels dirt or sand from a pile to a wheel barrow or truck (no digging required)	
LN 7	0 1 2 3 4 0 1 2 3 4 0 1 2 3 4 0 1 2 3 4	Rakes leaves	Learner will rake leaves into piles.	Can learner rake leaves into piles?		4= rakes leaves from entire yard into neat piles, 3= rakes at least half of yard into neat piles, 2= rakes half of yard but requires verbal prompts to make neat piles, 1= requires minimal physical prompting to rake leaves	
LN 8	0 1 2 3 4 0 1 2 3 4 0 1 2 3 4 0 1 2 3 4	Puts leaves into bags	Learner will put previously raked piles of leaves into paper garden bags for disposal.	Does learner put piles of leaves into yard bags?		4= places all leaf piles into bags, ties bags, and brings to street or other area for pick up, 3= places leaves into bags and brings to street but requires verbal prompts to tie bags, 2= requires verbal prompts to place leaves in bags, tie bags, and bring to street, 1= requires minimal physical prompts to place leaves in bag	
LN 9	0 1 2 0 1 2 0 1 2 0 1 2	Prunes shrubs and trees	Learner will prune shrubs and trees.	Can learner prune shrubs and trees?		2= clips branches from hedges, bushes, small plants so branches stick out in a uniform way, 1= clips branches as specified and designated by caregiver or supervisor	NEEDS CLOSE SUPERVISION

The AFLS® - Vocational Skills Protocol

The Assessment of Functional Living Skills - The AFLS®

Landscaping (Continued)

TASK	SCORE	TASK NAME	TASK OBJECTIVE	QUESTION	EXAMPLE	CRITERIA	COMMENT
LN 10	0 1 2 3 4 0 1 2 3 4 0 1 2 3 4 0 1 2 3 4	Applies fertilizer	Learner will apply fertilizer.	Can learner apply fertilizer?	Applies fertilizer to lawn, being careful not to apply too much or to spread on walkways or driveway	4= selects appropriate fertilizer and applies correct amount evenly and in appropriate areas, 3= applies given amount and type of fertilizer to designated area, 2= applies fertilizer to a designated area, 1= when provided with only verbal prompts, applies fertilizer to a designated area	NEEDS CLOSE SUPERVISION
LN 11	0 1 2 3 4 0 1 2 3 4 0 1 2 3 4 0 1 2 3 4	Applies chemicals to vegetation	Learner will apply chemicals to vegetation.	Can learner apply chemicals to vegetation?	Fungicides, insecticides, pesticides, etc.	4= selects chemicals, safely handles, and applies such as to distribute appropriate amount only to designated areas, 3= safely handles and applies given chemicals to designated area, 2= safely applies given chemicals to a designated area, 1= when provided with only verbal prompts, safely applies given chemicals to a designated area	NEEDS CLOSE SUPERVISION

Garden related machinery skills

TASK	SCORE	TASK NAME	TASK OBJECTIVE	QUESTION	EXAMPLE	CRITERIA	COMMENT
LN 12	0 1 2 3 4 0 1 2 3 4 0 1 2 3 4 0 1 2 3 4	Mows lawns	Learner will mow lawns.	Can learner mow lawns?	"Mows Lawn" means safely, slowly, without running over hard objects, being aware of rocks, curbs, etc., using the correct mower orientation on hills, etc.	4= clears lawn of obstacles, fills with gas and checks oil, starts engine, mows lawn, 3= clears obstacles from lawn, starts engine, and mows lawn, 2= when given a mower that has been started, safely mows lawn up to 1000 sq. ft. and turns off mower, 1= when given a mower that has been started, requires close supervision and verbal prompts to safely mow lawn of an area of 500 sq. ft.	NEEDS CLOSE SUPERVISION
LN 13	0 1 2 3 4 0 1 2 3 4 0 1 2 3 4 0 1 2 3 4	Uses hedger	Learner will use hedger to maintain hedges or shrubs.	Can learner use hedger to maintain hedges or shrubs?		4= starts and trims hedges with electric or gas powered hedger, and trims hedges with manual trimmer, 3= when provided with only verbal prompts, starts and trims hedges with electric or gas powered hedger, and trims hedges with manual trimmer, 2= trims hedges with manual hedge trimmer, 1= when provided with only verbal prompts, trims hedges with manual hedge trimmer	NEEDS CLOSE SUPERVISION

The AFLS® - Vocational Skills Protocol

The Assessment of Functional Living Skills - The AFLS®

Landscaping (Continued)

TASK	SCORE	TASK NAME	TASK OBJECTIVE	QUESTION	EXAMPLE	CRITERIA	COMMENT
LN 14	0 1 2 0 1 2 0 1 2 0 1 2	Uses edge trimmers	Learner will edge trimmers.	Can learner use edge trimmers?		2= trims edges of lawn using power or hand trimmer or edger, 1= requires close supervision and verbal prompts to edge lawn	
LN 15	0 1 2 3 4 0 1 2 3 4 0 1 2 3 4 0 1 2 3 4	Operates leaf blower	Learner will operate leaf blower.	Can learner operate leaf blower?		4= blows leaves, grass clippings, or other light yard debris into piles or acceptable designated area being mindful of people and property around blower and effects of flying materials, 3= blows leaves and yard debris into piles with only verbal prompts, 2= blows leaves and yard debris in a general direction, 1= blows leaves and yard debris in a general direction with only verbal prompts	

The AFLS® - Vocational Skills Protocol

Assessment Notes

Date: